Contents

CW00740520

ROYAL NAVY
Introduction......................... 3-7
Pennant Numbers...................... 9

Submarines
 - Vanguard Class.................... 12
 - Dreadnought Class................ 14
 - Astute Class.....................17
 - Trafalgar Class..................19
Aircraft Carriers
 - Queen Elizabeth Class........... 22
Landing Platform Dock
 - Albion Class.....................25
Destroyers
 - Daring Class (Type 45)........... 27
Frigates
 - Type 23 (ASW Variant)........... 29
 - Type 23 (GP Variant)............. 31
 - City Class (Type 26).............. 32
 - Inspiration Clas (Type 31)........ 35
Mine Countermeasures Vessels
 - Hunt Clas......................... 37
 - Sandown Class.................... 39
 - Mine Hunting Drone.............. 40
 - Mine Countermeasures Systems.. 41
Patrol Vessels
 - River II Class..................... 43
 - River Class....................... 45
 - Coastal Training Craft............47
 - Gibraltar Squadron............... 49
Survey Ships
 - Scott Class....................... 50
 - Echo Class....................... 52
 - Ice Patrol........................ 53
 - Inshore Survey................... 54
 - NavyX Support Vessel............ 55
 - NavyX Madfox.................... 56

Royal M
Ships f

ROYAL FLEET AUXILIARY
Introduction........................... 75
Pennant Numbers...................... 76

Tankers................................... 77
Stores/Specialist Ships................ 79

OPERATED FOR MoD
Tanker/Strategic Sealift/Ro-Ro........ 85

SERCO MARINE SERVICES
Introduction........................... 88
Fleet List................................ 89

Tugs..................................... 90
Coastal Craft & Trials Ships........... 100
Fleet Tenders, Multi-Purpose
Vessels & Support Craft.............. 103

OTHER VESSELS
Contract Vessels....................... 115
Army Vessels........................... 119
Border Force Vessels................... 120

THE FLEET AIR ARM
Aircraft of the F.A.A................... 125
Introduction........................... 126
Military Flying Training System....... 141

WEAPONRY
Weapons of the Royal Navy.......... 147

At the end of the line................. 155

British Warships & Auxiliaries

HMS Tamar

THE ROYAL NAVY

F or the Royal Navy a change of monarch might be a once in a lifetime occurrence, we had become blasé, believing that the Queen was and always would be on the throne. Her reign did however come to an end and now we must all become accustomed to phrase 'His Majesty's Ship' and 'King's Harbour Master'. Customs and traditions associated with a female monarch will transfer to those of a male King. Traditions in the Royal Navy are held in high regard and for the Senior Service to be attending to the departed Queen Elizabeth on her final journey from her laying in state to Westminster Abbey must have been an amazing experience for the 150 RN ratings involved. For the Royal Navy and Royal Fleet Auxiliary changes are happening too, but at a slower and mostly unseen rate. The advance of technology continues apace. Despite the change of Head of State, the day to day operations and running of the Royal Navy continue almost unaffected - most reassuringly. Despite the political turmoil of the last 18 months the defence budget is actually growing - for the first time in 40 years - from £48 billion a year to £100 billion by FY 2029-30.

In the last twelve months since the 2022 edition of *British Warships and Auxiliaries* we have seen some changes in the fleet, but nothing as compared to the almost seismic changes in the politics surrounding the character of the Royal Navy. In December 2021 the Fifth Special Report of the Defence Committee entitled, *"We're going to need a bigger Navy"*, not failing to give its readers a clear understanding of the challenges ahead.

The Government took two months to respond to the report's recommendations. It concluded that over the coming decade the Royal Navy will face an increasingly complex international security environment with the threat posed by Russia and China writ large. They also emphasised the growing threat posed by hypersonic weapon systems and from so called 'grey zone operations'. The Government continues to assert that the future of the Royal Navy is assured under their stewardship, with ambitious plans for the RN that will see the Navy given *'a significantly... and potentially leading role in the UK's security posture'*. To be fair, the RN is receiving an increased budget, rising from £7 billion in FY21/22 to £8.7 billion by FY30/31 in an effort to accelerate a drive to be more lethal, more available, and more sustainable. 'It is likely to be the Government's tool of choice to deliver its strategy of persistent engagement and competition below the threshold of warfare.' This challenging position also requires the Royal Navy to continue to maintain all of its existing commitments with the same resources, or less than before. Some of these resources are increasingly elderly, particularly in the case of the P2000 patrol boats.

The persistent global engagement taskings have principally, so far, been seen with the Batch 2 River-class offshore patrol boats TRENT and SPEY, forward deployed for five years to the Pacific, and sister ship MEDWAY permanently positioned in the Caribbean. The Royal Navy also maintains a permanent and expanding footprint in the Middle East. The Government asserts that through such deployments there is an increase in Maritime Domian Awareness (MDA), which generates a comprehensive understanding and provides a common operating picture for the United Kingdom and her allies and global partners.

Despite the very public and embarrassing failure of the aircraft carrier HMS PRINCE OF WALES to sail to the United States in the autumn of 2022, the Royal Navy is confident it will achieve Full Operating Capability (FOC) in December 2023, especially in light of the ordering of additional F-38B Lightning Strike aircraft.

The Defence sub-committee in its report of December 2021 stated that, *'The Navy cannot fulfil the full ambition of the Integrated Review with its current fleet. It needs more lower-end, adaptable vessels, like the planned Type 31 frigate, to fulfil the presence operations planned. A large part of the Government's plan to address this relies on increasing availability, as well as through the Type 32 programme. We are not convinced that increased availability can produce enough vessels to be relied upon in an emergency'*. In response, the then Liz Truss administration committed to grow the defence budget. Government future plans state that it intends to procure up to five Type 32 frigates in addition to the ongoing build of five Type 31 frigates. This is in addition to the eight Type 26 frigates. This will mean that by 2030 the total number of destroyers and frigates in the Royal Navy fleet will increase beyond the current 18. Liz Truss survived as Prime Minister for an historically short 45 days in office eventually being replaced by Rishi Sunak, who introduced a sweeping wave of government cuts. (At the time of writing it is unsure what this will mean for defence spending).

Another crucial element of the future shape of the fleet is the pressing need to replace the Solid Stores support ships in order to support Carrier Strike, although in November 2022 a British prime contractor was selected. There is also a requirement to build a single Multi Role Surveillance vessel to provide a *'Critical National Infrastructure protection capability'*. Additionally, six Multi-Role Support Ships (MRSS) are to be built to fully realise the benefits of Littoral Strike.

Crucially, the Government, and by default the Ministry of Defence, is determined to get more bang for its buck and have set in motion a plan to increase warship availability known as Project Renown. This multi-faceted project has set clear goals to reduce the number and length of time ships spend in dockyard hands. Run jointly by the DE&S and Navy Command, Project Renown has been stood up to cohere all ship availability activity from across DE&S Ships and Navy HQ under one project, to remove blockers and streamline processes that negatively impact ship availability. *"Since their launch, the Renown workstreams have successfully implemented some incredible improvements across DE&S and Navy including the T23 ARGYLL Hull and Structure Material Assessment (HASM) which has been reduced from a 12-month process to 12-week process offering significant time savings"*.

HMS Defender

Carrier Strike Group

The Government will continue with its tilt to the Indo-Pacific in 2023/24 and expects to deploy another Carrier Strike Group to the region within that timeframe subject to logistic and availability of suitable escort vessels. The tilt to focus on the region is driven by economics and an increasingly assertive and militaristic China. The Carrier Strike Capability is on track to achieve Full Operational Capability by December 2023. After that the MoD intends for an annual deployment of a CSG (either PRINCE OF WALES or QUEEN ELIZABETH). The destination of each deployment will be determined by the Senior Strategic Steering Group in the MoD before being endorsed by the Service Chiefs and Defence Ministers and those Ministers with vested interests in the CSG, such as the Foreign and Commonwealth Office and the Department for Trade and Industry. Each CSG deployment will be unique with set objectives and clearly defined operating areas. It should also be pointed out that CSG is much more than just a show of British naval power, it is Carrier Enabled Power Projection (CEPP), where further capabilities beyond carrier strike can be exploited such as humanitarian aid missions.

QUEEN ELIZABETH replaced PRINCE OF WALES in the summer of 2022 on the latter's United States deployment following a faulty main shaft which was discovered just after her departure from Portsmouth. The former carrier then interacted with American colleagues in the development and deployment of interchangeable innovative emergent technologies and tactics for their use. The MoD intends to upgrade the F-35B's lethality with new avionics and weapon systems particularly in the air-to-ground and anti-ship categories.

Submarines

Never has the often heard 'there are not enough ships in the Royal Navy' been more accurate than when describing the state of the Silent Service. With four Ballistic Missile (Boomer) boats and seven attack submarines, the Silent Service has insufficient mass to project global strike power. Even Australia plans on building a fleet of ten nuclear powered attack submarines against the British seven. Remember, seven may sound a lot, but only one third of that number could possibly be operationally deployed when one considers refits and training requirements.

The Dreadnought Ballistic Missile Submarine replacement programme is progressing well, but it will be at the end of this decade before the first of the class can be expected to enter the water. The Astute Class building programme is drawing to a close, but already advanced plans are being drawn for their eventual replacement.

Assault Ships

With out-of-service dates set for 2030 and 2031 ALBION and BULWARK are in the last decade of their service careers. These incredibly versatile workhorses of the Royal Marines offer vast capabilities that are hard to replicate with other assets. Design work on their replacements is at an early stage and although there is no funding available in the mid to long term for new construction, serious consideration must be made now to invest in sustaining this capability into the future. The provisional ideas for their replacement currently rests with a 'bought-off-the-shelf' Dutch design, itself based on the hull of a commercial ferry but fitted with military grade sensors and weaponry.

Destroyers

The propulsion troubles of the Type 45 destroyers have been well-documented and reported and I don't intend to go over them again here, suffice to say that within 2/3 years the refit programme to correct the problems will have been completed. It can only be hoped that the destroyers, post refit, will finally deliver on the promised capabilities. Furthermore, it is expected that the class will become the first in Europe to be equipped with anti-ballistic missile defences.

Frigates

The Royal Navy is still desperately short of frigates, although new Type 26 and Type 31 frigates are now finally under construction. Sadly, the building of the first Type 26 is slow. When HMS GLASGOW enters service she will have been in build for a decade. Ten years is too slow to build warships when China is building dozens of escorts annually. A decade is also an extremely long time as today's technology becomes dated sometimes within months.

Mine Warfare

Over the next five-ten years technology will have seen the traditional minesweeper and minehunter replaced with autonomous or semi-autonomous mine counter vessels that are cheaper to produce and acquire and will remove the human from one of the most dangerous and exacting tasks in naval warfare. Great strides have already been made in advancing this field within the Royal Navy. Further orders for future unmanned vessels are expected.

Patrol Boats

The Royal Navy has a healthy, if somewhat aged, collection of patrol boats. The newer River II-class vessels are distributed around the globe in an effort to extend the Royal Navy's, and by default, Britain's influence and commitment around the world. TAMAR and SPEY are on long term deployment to the Asia Pacific region, FORTH is the Falklands Guard ship, MEDWAY is in the Caribbean and TRENT is in the Mediterranean and African regions. The older River-class ships, MERSEY, SEVERN and TYNE remain in European waters to patrol and enforce Britain's Exclusive Economic Zone (EEZ) but have also been playing an increasingly active role in deterring and intercepting illegal immigration into Britain from France.

The old P2000 'Archer'-class patrol boats are increasingly getting long in the tooth but there are currently no plans on replacing these 1980's built vessels.

Survey

With the decommissioning of ECHO in 2022 the survey fleet now consists of just SCOTT, ENTERPRISE, MAGPIE and nominally the Ice Patrol ship PROTECTOR.

Patrick Boniface
Naval Author &
Editorial Correspondent Warship World
January 2023

HMS Diamond

SHIPS OF THE ROYAL NAVY
Pennant Numbers

Ship	P. No.	Page	Ship	P. No.	Page
Aircraft Carriers			*Batch 2*		
QUEEN ELIZABETH	R08	22	*BIRMINGHAM*	---	*32*
PRINCE OF WALES	R09	22	*SHEFFIELD*	---	*32*
			NEWCASTLE	---	*32*
Assault Ships			*LONDON*	---	*32*
ALBION	L14	25	*EDINBURGH*	---	*32*
BULWARK	L15	25			
			Frigates (Type 31)		
Destroyers (Type 45)			*FORMIDABLE*	---	*35*
DARING	D32	27	*BULLDOG*	---	*35*
DAUNTLESS	D33	27	*ACTIVE*	---	*35*
DIAMOND	D34	27	*VENTURER*	---	*35*
DRAGON	D35	27	*CAMPBELTOWN*	---	*35*
DEFENDER	D36	27			
DUNCAN	D37	27	**Submarines (Vanguard)**		
			VANGUARD	S28	12
Frigates (Type 23)			VICTORIOUS	S29	12
KENT	F78	29	VIGILANT	S30	12
PORTLAND	F79	29	VENGEANCE	S31	12
SUTHERLAND	F81	29			
SOMERSET	F82	29	**Submarines (Dreadnought)**		
ST ALBANS	F83	29	*DREADNOUGHT*	---	*14*
LANCASTER	F229	31	*VALIANT*	---	*14*
ARGYLL	F231	31	*WARSPITE*	---	*14*
IRON DUKE	F234	31	*KING GEORGE VI*	---	*14*
MONTROSE	F236	31			
WESTMINSTER	F237	29	**Submarines (Astute)**		
NORTHUMBERLAND	F238	29	ASTUTE	S119	17
RICHMOND	F239	29	AMBUSH	S120	17
			ARTFUL	S121	17
Frigates (Type 26)			AUDACIOUS	S122	17
GLASGOW	*F88*	*32*	*AGAMEMNON*	*S123*	*17*
CARDIFF	*F89*	*32*	ANSON	S124	17
BELFAST	*F90*	*32*	*AGINCOURT*	*S125*	*17*

Ship	P. No.	Page	Ship	P. No.	Page
Submarines (Trafalgar)			TRACKER	P274	47
TRIUMPH	S93	19	RAIDER	P275	47
			BLAZER	P279	47
Minehunters			DASHER	P280	47
LEDBURY	M30	37			
CATTISTOCK	M31	37	TYNE	P281	45
BROCKLESBY	M33	37	SEVERN	P282	45
MIDDLETON	M34	37	MERSEY	P283	45
CHIDDINGFOLD	M37	37			
HURWORTH	M39	37	PUNCHER	P291	48
PENZANCE	M106	39	CHARGER	P292	48
PEMBROKE	M107	39	RANGER	P293	48
GRIMSBY	M108	39	TRUMPETER	P294	48
BANGOR	M109	39			
SHOREHAM	M112	39	**Fast Patrol Boats (Gibraltar Squadron)**		
			CUTLASS	P295	49
Unmanned Minesweepers/Drones			DAGGER	P296	49
MINE HUNTING DRONES		40			
HEBE	---	41	**Survey Ships & RN Manned Auxiliaries**		
HARRIER	---	41	ENTERPRISE	H88	52
HAZARD	---	41	MAGPIE	H130	54
			SCOTT	H131	50
Patrol Craft			PROTECTOR	A173	53
EXPRESS	P163	47			
EXPLORER	P164	47	**NAVYX Support Vessel**		
EXAMPLE	P165	47	PATRICK BLACKETT	X01	55
EXPLOIT	P167	47			
			NAVYX Unmanned Surface Vessel		
FORTH	P222	43	MADFOX	---	56
MEDWAY	P223	43			
TRENT	P224	43			
TAMAR	P233	43			
SPEY	P234	43			
ARCHER	P264	47			
BITER	P270	47			
SMITER	P272	47			
PURSUER	P273	47			

Entries displayed in lighter typeface have yet to be completed

Royal Navy Submarines

HMS Vengeance

SUBMARINES
VANGUARD CLASS

Ship	Pennant Number	Completion Date	Builder
VANGUARD	S28	1992	VSEL
VICTORIOUS	S29	1994	VSEL
VIGILANT	S30	1997	VSEL
VENGEANCE	S31	1999	VSEL

Displacement: 15,980 tonnes (submerged) **Dimensions:** 149.9m x 12.8m x 12m
Machinery: 1 x Rolls-Royce PWR2 nuclear reactor; 2 GEC Turbines, 27,500 hp; single shaft; pump jet propulsor; two auxiliary retractable propulsion motors **Speed:** 25 + submerged **Armament:** 16 Tubes for Lockheed Trident 2 (D5) missiles, 4 Torpedo Tubes
Complement: 135 (14 officers)

Notes: These four submarines are the second generation of Britain's Independent Nuclear Deterrent. Since 1994, when VANGUARD, made her first deployment, this class have performed the silent and little reported role in total secrecy. Each submarine is armed with Trident 2 D5 missiles armed with independent nuclear re-entry vehicles. The number of these re-entry vehicles is being reassessed upwards following the publication of 2021's Integrated Strategic Defence Review.

The Vanguard class are all over 20 years old and will in due course be replaced in service by the new Dreadnought Class currently in build at BAE Systems Shipyard at Barrow-in-Furness. In the meantime, a life extension programme has been initiated to prolong the service careers of VIGILANT and VENGEANCE out to beyond 2028.

VANGUARD's refit has cost over £500million making it one of the most expensive Royal Navy refits ever undertaken.

The submarines are based at Faslane in Scotland and each boat has two captains and two crews which means the duty crew are out while their opposite number are training or on leave. At least one of these submarines are always on patrol somewhere in the world, a second is training and a third is undergoing routine maintenance. The fourth is usually in deep long-term refit or refuelling at Plymouth.

CROWN COPYRIGHT/MOD   **Astute-class submarine**

● ROLLS ROYCE

SUBMARINES
DREADNOUGHT CLASS

Ship	Pennant Number	Completion Date	Builder
DREADNOUGHT	-	-	*BAE Systems (Submarine)*
VALIANT	-	-	*BAE Systems (Submarine)*
WARSPITE	-	-	*BAE Systems (Submarine)*
KING GEORGE VI	-	-	*BAE Systems (Submarine)*

Displacement: 17,200 tonnes (submerged) **Dimensions:** 153.6m **Machinery:** 1 x Rolls-Royce PWR3 nuclear reactor; Turbo-electric drive, pump jet propulsor; single shaft **Speed:** -- **Armament:** 12 x ballistic missile tubes for 8-12 Lockheed Trident II D5 missiles, 4 x 21inch torpedo tubes for Spearfish heavyweight torpedoes **Complement:** 130

Notes: In May 2011, the Government announced the initial assessment phase for new submarines to replace the Vanguard-class submarines carrying Britain's Independent Nuclear Deterrent. The decision met with vehement objections from anti-nuclear campaigners and even those who objected to the cost of the programme put at £31 billion. At the same time the Government placed orders for long lead time items for the submarines including the nuclear reactors to power them and the specialist high strength steel required to maintain deep diving capabilities. Four years later after the Conservative Party's win at the 2015 elections, the Government committed to maintaining the deterrent with four so called 'Successor' submarines.

As the only shipyard in the United Kingdom able to build complex submarines BAE Systems was contracted to build the first submarine with construction of first of class DREADNOUGHT commencing on 6 October 2016. It is expected that DREADNOUGHT will enter service in 2028 in time to replace VANGUARD which will by then be 30 years old. Construction on the second in class, VALIANT commenced in September 2019.

The DREADNOUGHT Class will have an intended service life longer than the current VANGUARDs at between 35 to 40 years and will be powered by a nuclear reactor that will not need to be refuelled throughout the operational lifetime of the submarine, greatly reducing maintenance and running costs for the future fleet of four submarines. The missile tubes for the Trident missiles are the same as those being developed for the US Navy's Columbia-class of successor ballistic missile submarines.

The sensors aboard the submarines are expected to be state-of-the-art upon completion and boast items such as second-generation optronic masts instead of traditional periscopes. These masts will be constructed at Govan by Barr and Stroud who have been making submarine periscopes for almost one hundred years.

DREADNOUGHT and her sisters will be the largest submarines ever operated by the Royal Navy, and the most powerful. They also feature separate compartments for male and female personnel, a first on RN submarines. Special lighting arrangements aboard will imitate the day and night on the surface thus making life underwater easier to adapt to for submariners. The submarines will benefit from the installation of 'Fly-by-wire' technology equivalent to systems found on modern airliners. The Active Vehicle Control Management System will oversee all major aspects of the submarines manoeuvring including heading, pitch, depth, and buoyancy. The new system is being developed by BAE Systems Controls and Avionics at their site in Rochester in Kent and will use computers to supplement the work of 'planesmen' operating the submarines, in what is a very physically and mentally demanding role aboard.

Warhead and missile
The UK warhead will be integrated with the US supplied Mark 7 aeroshell to ensure it remains compatible with the Trident II D5 missile and delivered in parallel with the US W93/Mk7 warhead programme. The transition of the current Mark 4 warhead to the Mark 4A is ongoing, addressing obsolescence to ensure the UK continue to have a safe, secure, and available stockpile until the UK replacement warhead is available in the 2030s. The UK also continues to participate with US partners on work to extend the life of the Trident II D5 missiles. These life extension programmes will address obsolescence and continue to provide sufficient missile packages, including spares, to support the UK's current stock entitlement.

International collaboration
In addition to working closely with the US Navy and American authorities the Royal Navy is also collaborating with the French Navy. *"We continue to cooperate with France under the TEUTATES Treaty, signed in November 2010, working together on the technology associated with the nuclear stockpile stewardship in support of our respective independent nuclear deterrent capabilities, in full compliance with our international obligations. Progress continues to be made with the delivery of the experimental hydrodynamic capability at Epure in France and associated capabilities at AWE which*

will allow both the UK and France to conduct independent experiments ensuring both nations' nuclear weapons remain safe and effective."

Reactors and Missile tubes

Rolls-Royce Submarines continue to make good progress with the manufacture of the nuclear propulsion power plants, the Pressurised Water Reactor 3, for all four Dreadnought-class submarines. The procurement on long lead items and other early work for the remaining submarines in the Class, WARSPITE and KING GEORGE VI, continues in line with the overall programme schedule.

As previously reported, production and delivery of the Missile Tubes (MT) to form part of the Common Missile Compartment have been subject to quality shortfalls across the supply chain resulting in their delayed delivery. All 12 missile tubes for HMS DREADNOUGHT have now been delivered to the BAE Systems Barrow shipyard.

CROWN COPYRIGHT/MOD   **HMS Audacious**

HMS Astute

ASTUTE CLASS

Ship	Pennant Number	Completion Date	Builder
ASTUTE	S119	2007	BAE Systems (Submarine)
AMBUSH	S120	2012	BAE Systems (Submarine)
ARTFUL	S121	2015	BAE Systems (Submarine)
AUDACIOUS	S122	2018	BAE Systems (Submarine)
ANSON	S124	2021	BAE Systems (Submarine)
AGAMEMNON	*S123*	*2023*	*BAE Submarine Solutions*
AGINCOURT	*S125*	*2026*	*BAE Submarine Solutions*

Displacement: 7,400 tonnes (7,800 tonnes submerged) **Dimensions:** 97m x 11.2m x 9.5m **Machinery:** Rolls-Royce PWR2; 2 Alsthom Turbines, 27,500 hp; single shaft; pump jet propulsor; two motors for emergency drive; one auxiliary retractable propellor **Speed:** 29+ submerged **Armament:** 6 Torpedo Tubes; Spearfish torpedoes; Tomahawk cruise missiles for a payload of 38 weapons **Complement:** 110 (including 12 Officers)

Notes: This class of nuclear-powered submarines are the direct successors to the extremely successful Trafalgar-class vessels but were designed to incorporate a raft of innovative technologies and systems unheard of when the Trafalgar's were in build.

The Astute Class are designed to fulfil a wide-range of strategic and tactical roles within the Royal Navy from anti-ship and anti-submarine warfare, surveillance and intelligence gathering to support of land forces and the delivery of long-range ordnance (Tomahawk cruise missiles) to targets deep within enemy territories. Each submarine has a dock down capability allowing divers to operate from the boat whilst it remains submerged and undetected. This is in addition to the Chalfont dry-deck hangar which can be loaded and unloaded onto the back of the submarines for specialised swimmer teams for stand-off insertion missions for specialist forces.

At the heart of the Astute-class submarines is the BAE Common Combat System (CCS) which was first fully evaluated aboard ARTFUL in February 2016. Essentially the CCS is a computerised brain within the submarine that controls all its sensors in an analogous way to a human nervous system interacts with its ears, eyes, and nose. The system can interpret sonar readings and coordinate appropriate attacks on enemy submarines accordingly. The system was introduced from build on AUDACIOUS and on all new build submarines after that, with retrofitting on older boats at scheduled refit dates.

AUDACIOUS commissioned into service with the Royal Navy on 23 September 2021 following a lengthy build and sea trials programme. The Royal Navy rarely makes public statements about submarine construction programmes. ANSON was accepted into the Royal Navy on 31 August 2022 in the presence of then Prime Minister Boris Johnson and Australian Deputy Prime Minister Richard Marles, who through the AUKUS agreement, have set their sights on building up to ten nuclear powered submarines. Construction of the remaining two Astute-class submarines - AGAMEMNON and AGINCOURT is proceeding on schedule with the latter's expected handover to be sometime in 2026. The construction programme for the class has seen significant improvement since the first three vessels were launched.

CROWN COPYRIGHT/MOD   HMS Anson

HMS Triumph

TRAFALGAR CLASS

Ship	Pennant Number	Completion Date	Builder
TRIUMPH	S93	1991	Vickers

Displacement: 4,500 tonnes (5,298 tonnes submerged) **Dimensions:** 85.4m x 9.8m x 9.5m **Machinery:** Rolls-Royce PWR1; 2 GEC Turbines, 15,000 hp; single shaft; pump jet propulsor; one motor for emergency drive - retractable propellor **Speed:** 30+ dived **Armament:** 5 Torpedo Tubes; Spearfish torpedoes; Tomahawk cruise missiles for a payload of 24 weapons **Complement:** 130

Notes: TRIUMPH is the last survivor of a class of seven nuclear attack submarines and should, by rights, already have been removed from service, but delays in the Astute Class programme have meant that she has been retained in active service beyond original out of service dates. The Trafalgar Class has, since the mid-1980s, been the backbone of the Royal Navy's silent service, but even in their autumn years the submarines still have a vital role to play in Britain's defence. TRIUMPH was scheduled to end her career in 2022, but late 2022 she completed a large refit at Devonport Dockyard that will see her life extended out to 2024/25.

In May 2022, both HMS TALENT and HMS TRENCHANT were decommissioned at Devonport Naval Base. Crews from both nuclear-powered attack boats paraded in Plymouth for the final time in front of HRH The Princess Royal - HMS TALENT's patron - as well as high-profile guests and former commanding officers. TRENCHANT's operational career came to an end in 2021 while TALENT completed her final patrol in spring 2022. Both boats served for 32 years with distinction. As hunter-killer submarines, it was their mission to protect first Polaris, now Trident – the country's Strategic Nuclear Deterrent – and to detect, track and classify targets.

The boats are capable of gaining intelligence, covertly inserting troops ashore, or striking at enemy submarines and ships with Spearfish torpedoes and targets ashore with Tomahawk cruise missiles.

Project CETUS

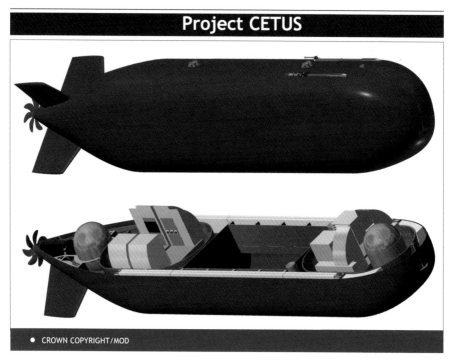

CROWN COPYRIGHT/MOD

Notes: In late 2022 the Ministry of Defence awarded a £15.4 million contract to Plymouth-based tech firm MSubs to develop the largest unmanned and most complex demonstrator submarine for the principal purpose of protecting Great Britain's underwater lines of communication and energy pipelines and cables. When it enters service the vehicle will be the largest uncrewed submarine of its type operated by any European nation. The project has been given the name Project CETUS, named after a mythological sea creature.

Project CETUS is the first logical step in developing an independent operational autonomous submarine that can be utilised alongside existing submarines, such as the Astutes and their successors, or crucially independently. Another aspect of the vehicle being crewless is that the submarine can operate at considerably deeper depths than a comparable manned submarine. Cetus will also be able to cover around 1,000 miles in a single mission profile.

The submarine will be 12 metres long and 2.2 metres in diameter, or around the size of a double decker bus and weigh approximately 17 tonnes. Each submarine will be reconfigurable to match mission requirements with a payload bay that can be additionally extended by adding another section, doubling the capacity.

Royal Navy Warship

HMS Montrose

HMS Queen Elizabeth

AIRCRAFT CARRIER
QUEEN ELIZABETH CLASS

Ship	Pennant Number	Completion Date	Builder
QUEEN ELIZABETH	R08	2017	Aircraft Carrier Alliance
PRINCE OF WALES	R09	2019	Aircraft Carrier Alliance

Displacement: 65,500 tonnes FL **Dimensions:** 282.9m x 38.8m x 11m **Machinery:** Integrated Full Electric Propulsion; 2 RR MT30 GT alternators, 93,870 hp (70 MW), 4 Wärtsilä DG, 53,064 hp (39.6 MW); 4 induction motors, 53,640 hp (40 MW); 2 shafts **Speed:** 26 knots **Armament:** 3 x Phalanx, 4 x 30mm **Aircraft:** Up to 36 x F-35B Lightning and 4 x Merlin ASaC (Crowsnest). Typical mix could be 12-24 F-35B and various helicopters which could include Merlin, Chinook, Wildcat and Apache **Complement:** 686 + 830 Air Group

Notes: These 65,000 tonnes aircraft carriers are the largest and most complex surface vessels ever designed, built, and operated by the Royal Navy. Each ship can accommodate all military helicopter types currently in the British armed forces (Navy, Army and Air Force) plus up to 40 F-35B Lightning II Joint Strike Fighters. Since December 2020, the United Kingdom has had a Carrier Strike capability resting in these two ships.

In March 2022 HMS QUEEN ELIZABETH returned to the serene waters of the Firth of Clyde for the second time since her launch in July 2014. She was last seen on the Clyde in March 2021 when she sailed to Loch Long to be loaded with ammunition ahead of her successful deployment with the Carrier Strike Group. She returned to Glen Mallan ammunitioning jetty which completed a £67 million upgrade to accommodate the Royal Navy's Queen Elizabeth Carriers in 2021.

In November 2022 five of the most powerful warships in the NATO alliance – plus their supporting carrier strike groups – were operating in Atlantic and Mediterranean waters in a demonstration of NATO unity. The five carriers were HMS QUEEN ELIZABETH operating in northern European waters; USS GEORGE H W BUSH on operations in the Adriatic, USS GERALD R FORD at anchor in Stokes Bay, Gosport, on a short visit to Portsmouth; France's FS CHARLES DE GAULLE and Italy's ITS CAVOUR both in the Mediterranean.

Although each nation's forces are operating in support of their own mission objectives and are part of their regularly scheduled activities, the advanced cooperation is part of a demonstration of NATO unity and the collective defence of the Alliance.

In December 2022 QUEEN ELIZABETH and her Carrier Strike Group returned home after three weeks of flying operations in the North Sea and Scandinavia. She was at the heart of a task force consisting of five warships, F-35B Lightning jets from 617 Squadron and Wildcat and Merlin helicopters. HMS DIAMOND, HMS KENT, HMS RICHMOND and RFA TIDESURGE formed a protective ring of steel around the aircraft carrier as jets and helicopters flew sorties round the clock, day and night.

The group stopped in Oslo, Norway's capital, after completing one of the narrowest harbour entries in her lifetime. The 60-mile journey through Oslo fjord from the Skagerrak (the strait running between the coasts of Denmark, Norway and Sweden) saw the UK's flagship carefully manoeuvered through the Drøbak Sound – which is about 1000m or nine football pitches wide and 11 miles long – into the inner fjord.

● DEREK FOX   **HMS Prince of Wales (left) and HMS Queen Elizabeth**

HMS Prince of Wales

On 1 January 2022 the Royal Navy assumed command of the maritime part of NATO's Response Force (NRF) from the French Marine Nationale, with PRINCE OF WALES serving as command ship for the international task group. For the next 12 months she would have been responsible for leading the alliance's Maritime High Readiness Force – an international task group formed to deal with major global events, but this was not to be. Their first mission was leading naval involvement COLD RESPONSE 22, a large-scale Norwegian-led NATO exercise. As the year moved on, staff also helped train and ready the Turkish Navy who will assume command of the NRF from the UK in 2023.

On 27 August 2022, she left her home port of Portsmouth for exercises off the East coast of the US. As soon as she passed the Isle of Wight, after a grand send-off for her transatlantic voyage, she sustained a shaft failure crippling the ship. Several media outlets reported different causes of the failure including that the propellor may have hit an underwater buoy or that she left the approach channel and hit a sandbank, and even that she hit a Russian submarine! For almost a week she was anchored off the UK coast while investigations took place about the cause of the accident. Towed by tugs, she finally returned to Portsmouth where a dive inspection revealed that a coupling on her starboard shaft had failed, resulting in both shaft and rudder damage. It was planned that her starboard propellor - weighing a staggering 33 tonnes - would be pulled while berthed at Portsmouth and that she would leave for Rosyth, Scotland, on 3 October. But technical issues pushed back her departure until 8 October when she departed Portsmouth to return to Rosyth, where she would enter drydock for repairs.

The initial assessment showed that coupling that joins the final two sections of the shaft had failed which is an extremely unusual fault. The Royal Navy is still struggling with repairs to HMS PRINCE OF WALES. As reported in the November/December issue of Warship World, the repairs were scheduled to take six weeks but a spokesperson for the Royal Navy has recently said: "Repairs to HMS PRINCE OF WALES' starboard shaft are expected to be completed by Spring 2023. The ship will then return to Portsmouth for a pre-planned maintenance period.

HMS Albion

LANDING PLATFORM DOCK
ALBION CLASS

Ship	Pennant Number	Completion Date	Builder
ALBION	L14	2003	BAE Systems
BULWARK	L15	2004	BAE Systems

Displacement: 18,797 tonnes FL, 21,500 tonnes (flooded) Dimensions 176m x 28.9m x 7.1m
Machinery: Diesel-electric; 2 Wärtsilä Vasa 32E DG, 17,000 hp (12.5 MW); 2 Wärtsilä Vasa 32LNE DG, 4,216 hp (3.1 MW); 2 motors; 2 shafts; 1 bow thruster Speed: 18 knots
Armament: 2 x CIWS, 2 x 20mm guns (single) Complement: 325 Military Lift 303 troops, with an overload capacity of a further 405

Notes: These highly versatile vessels provide the Royal Navy with its amphibious punch and were designed with the function of landing Royal Marines ashore by air and by sea. They also have extensive command and control facilities and can operate as flagships for operations and major deployments.

Each ship has deck capacity for up to six Army Challenger main battle tanks or around 30 armoured all-terrain vehicles. A floodable well dock aft can accommodate four LCU Mk10 utility landing craft, while four smaller LCVP Mk5B landing craft are carried on davits.

ALBION and BULWARK have a large flight deck capable of receiving all British and most Allied helicopter types currently in service but neither have hangar facilities. The flight deck is arranged with two landing spots for simultaneous operation of two RAF Chinook helicopters.

It is Royal Navy policy to have one of these vessels operational while the other is retained in reserve or refit. In 2017 ALBION re-emerged since being laid up since 2012 and assumed the role of Fleet Flagship, subsequently passed onto HMS QUEEN ELIZABETH in 2020.

BULWARK is currently slowly regenerating at Devonport and is expected to replace her sister ship in the operational fleet in this and ALBION will go into reserve for another five years before being refitted for further service for what is expected to be her last commission between 2028-2033.

ALBION and BULWARK's out of service dates are 2033 and 2034. Defence Procurement Minister Jeremy Quinn MP in 2022 stated in a written reply to another MP that plans for a replacement are now underway with the design at *"concept stage"*. These may include purchasing an off-the-shelf European design of LPD to speed up the delivery of this enormously useful and versatile capability.

● CROWN COPYRIGHT/MOD **HMS Albion**

● DEREK FOX HMS Diamond

DESTROYERS
DARING CLASS (Type 45)

Ship	Pennant Number	Completion Date	Builder
DARING	D32	2008	BVT Surface Fleet
DAUNTLESS	D33	2008	BVT Surface Fleet
DIAMOND	D34	2009	BVT Surface Fleet
DRAGON	D35	2011	BVT Surface Fleet
DEFENDER	D36	2012	BVT Surface Fleet
DUNCAN	D37	2013	BVT Surface Fleet

Displacement: 7,350 tonnes **Dimensions:** 152.4m x 21.2m x 5.7m **Machinery:** Integrated Electric Propulsion; 2 RR WR-21 GT alternators, 67,600 hp (49.7 MW); 2 Wärtsilä DG (4 MW); 2 Converteam motors (40 MW); 2 shafts **Speed:** 29 knots **Armament:** 1 - 4.5-inch gun, 2 x Quad Harpoon missile launchers (on four ships), Sea Viper missile system comprising Sylver VLS with combination of up to 48 Aster 15 and Aster 30 missiles, 2 x Vulcan Phalanx (fitted as required) **Aircraft:** Wildcat or Merlin **Complement:** 190 (with space for 235)

Notes: These six vessels were originally planned to replace the preceding Type 42 destroyers on a ship-for-ship basis but the original plan to buy twelve (down from 14 Type 42s) was cut to 8 and then finally six in June 2008 with all these ships entering service by 2013.

Central to the success of the design is its 18,000mph Sea Viper anti-aircraft missile system which can knock-out enemy targets at ranges up to 70 miles from the ship. This potent weapon is linked to the powerful Sampson Multi-Function Radar that can track hundreds of targets at previously unheard distances. The latest version of the S1850M long range radar can track up to 1,000 air targets at around 400 kilometres in 3D.

It was claimed at the time of their inception that with these key systems the six destroyers could cover more surface area than a comparable Type 42 and thus fewer hulls were required. Or could it have been the £1 billion price tag for each of the new warships?

Since their first acceptance into service, the Type 45 destroyers received criticism over the perceived weakness of their propulsion plants. They use a pioneering Integrated Electric Propulsion (IEP) system – the first time that it has been used in a major warship design. The system comprises GE alternators driven by two Rolls-Royce WR-21 gas turbines, with two Wärtsilä 12V200 diesel generators providing electrical power at 4,160V to a GE high voltage system. The high voltage system is then used to provide power to the two GE Power Conversion advanced motors with outputs of 20MW each.

As long ago as 2016 the Government admitted that the Northrop Grumman intercooler was unreliable and prone to breaking down, particularly in hot and dry conditions. The solution was settled upon with a March 2018 announcement stating that Cammell Laird shipyard in Birkenhead would undertake restorative refits on all six ships by replacing their faulty diesel engines with three new ones, therefore adding another layer of redundancy into the system. This series of initiatives was christened '*The Power Improvement Project for the Type 45*'. The programme of rectification and upgrading of these ships is almost complete.

On May 24, 2022, the Ministry of Defence announced that the Type 45 destroyers will be refitted with upgraded sensors and weaponry to intercept and destroy ballistic missiles. The Ballistic Missile Defence Capability (BMD) will be a major milestone in the history of the class as they will become the first European warships to field this capability, that up till now was the preserve of the United States, Russia and Japan. The Aster 30 Block 1NT (New Technology) missile has been developed for the land based SAMP-T Ballistic missile defence system and has been adapted for naval use through the Sylver VLS and offering a range of some 600 kilometres. The need for greater accuracy and range has been met with the Aster 30 Block 1NT missiles being fitted with a new Ka-band radar seeker head. Future developments of the Aster Block 2 missile are said to be continuing with advertised ranges out to 3,000 kilometres. Existing Royal Navy stockpiles of Aster missiles will be upgraded to Block 1 standard and will differ slightly from their French and Italian counterparts.

BMD is part of an ongoing programme of incremental improvements to the Type 45 destroyers that also includes the Sea Viper Evolution programme (SV-E) that have seen significant upgrades made to the six Type 45 destroyer's Sampson multi-function radar (MFR). It is also expected that the current capacity of 48 missiles carried by each Type 45 destroyer will be increased to 72 between 2026 and 2032.

HMS Portland

FRIGATES
TYPE 23 (ASW Variant)

Ship	Pennant Number	Completion Date	Builder
KENT	F78	2000	Yarrow
PORTLAND	F79	2000	Yarrow
SUTHERLAND	F81	1997	Yarrow
SOMERSET	F82	1996	Yarrow
ST ALBANS	F83	2001	Yarrow
WESTMINSTER	F237	1993	Swan Hunter
NORTHUMBERLAND	F238	1994	Swan Hunter
RICHMOND	F239	1994	Swan Hunter

Displacement: 4,900 tonnes **Dimensions:** 133m x 16.1m x 5.5m **Machinery:** CODLAG; 2 RR Spey GT, 31,100 hp (23.2 MW); 4 Paxman diesels 8,100 hp (6 MW); 2 GEC motors, 4,000 hp (3 MW); 2 shafts **Speed:** 28 knots **Armament:** Harpoon or Sea Ceptor; 1 x 4.5-inch gun, 2 x single 30mm guns, 2 x twin (324 mm) Sting Ray Torpedo Tubes **Aircraft:** Wildcat or Merlin helicopter **Complement:** 185

Notes: The Type 23 provide the backbone to the Royal Navy's surface fleet and, whilst primarily designed for the anti-submarine warfare conditions found at the end of the Cold War, have proven to be capable general-purpose vessels in the new technologically dominated battlespace. When originally conceived in the early 1980s the Type 23 was to have been a relatively limited, affordable escort, but following the lessons of the Falklands War of 1982 the design was recast and grew out of all recognition to the first straightforward design concepts. With this extra growth came a parallel increase in the cost of acquisition of platforms and, while the original ships had an expected service life of little more than twelve years, that figure now encompasses the age of the oldest Type 23 ARGYLL to the newest ST ALBANS.

The Royal Navy's ambition is to keep these relatively old vessels at the forefront of technology and to bridge the gap between the first of the class leaving service and the introduction into service of the first of the new Type 26 City-class frigates from around 2025. To achieve this the ships have received a LIFEX (Life Extension) programme of retrofits. This capability sustainment includes, but is not limited to, the removal of the legacy Seawolf anti-aircraft missile and its replacement with the more modern and capable Seaceptor missiles, extensive hull maintenance and weapon and sensor upgrades to allow the ships to keep pace with the latest military developments around the globe.

Crucial to the LIFEX programme is work on the ship's Power Generation Machinery Upgrade (PGMU) which involves the replacement of four main propulsion diesel generator sets. Another, less well publicised aspect of the refit is the installation of new 'stealth' technologies designed to assist in the detection of enemy deep submerged submarines and furthermore means to defend the frigates from detection themselves by the very submarines they are tracking. Work on the Type 23s has all been carried out at Babcock's at Devonport Dockyard where over 1,000 people work on the programme for the Ministry of Defence with each ship programme usually taking between 18-24 months to complete.

The planned decommissioning dates are: WESTMINSTER (2028); NORTHUMBERLAND (2029); RICHMOND (2030); SOMERSET (2031); SUTHERLAND (2032); KENT (2033); PORTLAND (2034) and ST ALBANS (2035).

F238

GORDON BRODIE   **HMS Northumberland**

HMS Lancaster

FRIGATES
TYPE 23 (GP Variant)

Ship	Pennant Number	Completion Date	Builder
LANCASTER	F229	1991	Yarrow
ARGYLL	F231	1991	Yarrow
IRON DUKE	F234	1992	Yarrow
MONTROSE	F236	1993	Yarrow

Displacement: 4,900 tonnes **Dimensions:** 133m x 16.1m x 5.5m **Machinery:** CODLAG; 2 RR Spey GT, 31,100 hp (23.2 MW); 4 Paxman diesels 8,100 hp (6 MW); 2 GEC motors, 4,000 hp (3 MW); 2 shafts **Speed:** 28 knots **Armament:** Harpoon or Sea Ceptor; 1 - 4.5-inch gun, 2 x single 30mm guns, 2 x twin (324 mm) Sting Ray Torpedo Tubes **Aircraft:** Wildcat or Merlin helicopter **Complement:** 185

Notes: These ships have not been retrofitted with the advanced Type 2037 sonar system and operate in the General-Purpose role. As these ships are the oldest Type 23s in the fleet it is expected that they will be the first to replaced by the new Type 31 frigates when they enter service. In 2019 IRON DUKE was towed to Plymouth for her LIFEX refit that is expected to see her fitted with a new 3D Artisan radar and air defence weapon system and Sea Ceptor missiles replacing her legacy Seawolf.

MONMOUTH was withdrawn from service in 2021 and MONTROSE will leave service in April 2023. The out of service dates for the remaining three ships remain ARGYLL (2023), LANCASTER (2024) and IRON DUKE (2025).

FRIGATES
CITY CLASS (Type 26)

Ship	Pennant Number	Completion Date	Builder
GLASGOW	*F88*	-	*BAE Systems Glasgow*
CARDIFF	*F89*	-	*BAE Systems Glasgow*
BELFAST	*F90*	-	*BAE Systems Glasgow*
Batch 2			
BIRMINGHAM	-	-	*BAE Systems Glasgow*
SHEFFIELD	-	-	*BAE Systems Glasgow*
NEWCASTLE	-	-	*BAE Systems Glasgow*
LONDON	-	-	*BAE Systems Glasgow*
EDINBURGH	-	-	*BAE Systems Glasgow*

Displacement: 8,000+ tonnes full load **Dimensions:** 149.9m x 20.8m **Machinery:** CODLOG; 2 shafts **Speed:** 26 knots **Range:** 7,000 nautical miles **Armament:** 12-cell VLS for 48 Sea Ceptor anti-air missiles, 24-cell Mk 41 VLS for Tomahawk, 1 x 5 inch 62 calibre Mk 45 naval gun, 2 x 30mm DS30M Mk2 guns, 2 x Phalanx CIES, 2 x miniguns, 4 x general purpose machine guns **Aircraft:** up to two helicopters (Wildcat) armed with 4 x anti-ship missiles, or 2 anti-submarine torpedoes, 20 Martlet multi-role air-to-surface missiles and Mk 11 depth charges or 1 x Merlin armed with 4 anti-submarine torpedoes **Complement:** 157 (with space for 208)

Notes: The long-drawn-out timeframe associated with the design and development of modern warships is plain to see in the development of the Type 26 or City-class frigates.

Planning for the replacement of the Type 22 and Type 23 frigates of the surface fleet started in 1998 with the commencement of the Future Surface Combatant (FSC) programme. The research trimaran RV TRITON was procured but in the end more conventional hull designs were chosen over radical innovations. In March 2005, two versions of the FSC were announced showing a two-class series of ships, one 'Medium Sized Vessel Derivative' for service in the 2016-19 timeframe and a more capable 'Versatile Surface Combatant' entering service from around 2023.

Defence officials, trying to get the best bang for their buck circa 2006, explored the possibilities of extracting the maximum synergies between the FSC and the need for replacement survey ships and minesweepers under the Sustained Surface Combatant Capability (S2C2) programme. There were three clear requirements for the Royal Navy at this time: C1 - a high-end anti-submarine dedicated vessel of around 6,000 tonnes displacement; C2 - a general-purpose platform of around 4-5,000 tonnes and C3, a Global Corvette which could replace most of the survey and mine warfare fleet in service.

In 2008 the FSC concept was brought forward in the budget at the expense of building another pair of Type 45 destroyers. Detailed design work on the new C1 and C2 concepts was handed over to BAE Systems in 2009. Each vessel would have an expected lifespan of 25 years with one being built every year for a total of 18 (10C1 and 8C2 variants).

Crucially the first of the FSCs were to have entered service in 2020. In 2020 the mine warfare aspect of the programme was dropped in favour of the Mine Countermeasures, Hydrography and Patrol Capability (MHPC) programme. In 2010 FSC became the Global Combat Ship and expectations were high that the first of class might be in service by 2021.

2010, however, was the year of the 2010 Strategic Defence and Security Review that stripped the Royal Navy of the highly capable Type 22 frigates and ARK ROYAL, and the Harrier jump jets. Orders for new ships were farmed off into the long grass for a while and the programme started to slip. The Government's decision to reduce the size of the surface fleet to just 19 escorts also meant that there would be fewer orders for the Global Combat Ship. The Government also insisted that the specifications for the Global Combat Ship be pared down on a cost saving exercise from around £500m per ship to around £250m - £350m per vessel. However, this decision was later recinded and in February 2015 BAE Systems signed a £859m MoD contract to continue development and work towards manufacture. Ultimately, on 2 July 2017 BAE Systems was awarded a £3.7 billion contract for the first three ships at their Govan shipyard on the Clyde.

In design, the Global Combat Ship has modularity and flexibility as key capability enhancers to allow the ships to operate in as wide a range of scenarios as possible, from full-scale war to maritime security, counter piracy or humanitarian relief. Through life support offered by BAE Systems is another key component in ensuring that the hulls remain relevant throughout the next three decades as technology develops and can be replaced relatively easily. The Royal Navy Type 26 ships will be equipped with the Type 997 Artisan 3D search radar and the Sea Ceptor (CAMM) anti air-defence missile system launched via 48 vertical launch system (VLS) canisters. An additional 24-cell Mk 41 'strike length VLS' cells are positioned forward of the bridge and can accommodate long-range strike weapons such as Tomahawk land-attack cruise missiles and future long-range supersonic anti-ship and anti-land weapons.

The City Class's primary role remains that of anti-submarine warfare and for this the ship's hulls have been designed to be acoustically quiet. They are equipped with powerful Ultra Electronics Type 2150 next generation bow mounted sonar and a Sonar 2087 towed array. Each ship will be up-gunned from the current 4.5 inch calibre gun of the Type 23s and Type 45s to mount a NATO standard BAE 5inch, 62 calibre Mk 45 naval gun. For propulsion, the Type 26s will feature a gas turbine direct drive and four high speed diesel generators driving a pair of electric motors in a combined diesel-electric or gas (CODLOG) configuration.

The first-of-class was named GLASGOW, with steel being cut in her construction on 20 July 2017. By late 2021 the first three members of the class were in various stages of construction. GLASGOW is expected to be commissioned in 2028 which will mean that she took more than a decade to build and commission into service! In mid-November 2022 the £4.2 billion order for the five ships of Batch 2 was confirmed by the UK Government.

The Type 26 design has been chosen by Canada and Australia as the basis for their frigate replacement programmes, respectively the Canadian Surface Combatant and the Hunter Class. Canada is building up to 15 ships and Australia nine. Both nations are procuring many more hulls than the Royal Navy.

CROWN COPYRIGHT/MOD

Future HMS Glasgow

Future HMS Venturer

FRIGATES
INSPIRATION CLASS (Type 31)

Ship	Pennant Number	Completion Date	Builder
VENTURER	-	Building	Babcock International
BULLDOG	-	Ordered	Babcock International
CAMPBELTOWN	-	Ordered	Babcock International
FORMIDABLE	-	Ordered	Babcock International
ACTIVE	-	Building	Babcock International

Displacement: 5,700 tonnes **Dimensions:** 138.7m x 19.8m x 5m **Machinery:** 4 x Rolls Royce/MTU 20V 8000 M71 diesel engines, 4 x Rolls Royce/MTU 16V 2000 M41B generators = 32+ MW electric propulsion system **Speed:** 28+ knots **Range:** 9,000 nautical miles **Armament:** Bofors 57mm Mk 3 naval gun, 2 x 40mm guns, 4 x 7.62 machine guns, 4 x 7.62mm mini guns, up to 24 cell Sea Ceptor anti-aircraft missiles **Aircraft:** Either a single AugustaWestland Wildcat HMA2 or AugustaWestland Merlin Mk 2 helicopter **Complement:** 80-100 (accommodation for up to 160)

Notes: Construction of the first components for VENTURER commenced on 23 September 2021 in the specially built £31.5 million state-of-the-art 147-metre long and 30 metre high construction hall at Rosyth Dockyard. The official laying of her keel took place on 26th April 2022. To speed construction, and possibly to reduce costs in the process, two ships of the class can be built simultaneously side by side in this vast building. The class evolved from the 2010 Strategic Defence and Security Review and emerging from the Global Combat Ship these future vessels will complement the Type 32 frigate and the more capable Type 26 frigates. They are expected to enter service in the late 2020s. The class is the first to be ordered under the so-called Pathfinder programmes established under the auspices of the National Shipbuilding Programme that aims to create and maintain a steady and healthy drumbeat of warship construction across the United Kingdom rather than the drip feed that has been the norm for near on four decades. Under the Pathfinder programmes shipyards across the country will be able to bid on programmes that will sustain employment and innovative technological progress in shipbuilding whilst updating and modernising the Royal Navy's core escort fleet, which has taken an unprecedented hammering across a succession of defence reviews since the end of World War Two.

The Type 31e has been designed to fit in the capability gap roughly between the Type 26 frigates and those of the River II-class offshore patrol vessels. That being said these frigates will not be Second Rate vessels of old as they will be equipped with the latest technology and weaponry such as a Bofors 57mm Mk 3 naval gun, 40mm guns and the Sea Ceptor anti-air missile system in vertical launch tubes.

The Type 31e is based on Babcock's Arrowhead 140 design and are modular, so it is likely that they may be readily reconfigurable to match specific mission or deployment profiles. These mission bays will be flexible and adaptable at short notice will allow these vessels to provide a reassuring presence to British Overseas Territories and be capable of worldwide deployment on long-term missions in support of British political, security, military and economic aims.

HMS VENTURER is scheduled to be launched this year but her entry into service will be 2027. Interestingly the names chosen for this class were chosen to reflect five key themes around future Royal Navy missions.

• BABCOCK INTERNATIONAL

Type 31

HMS Ledbury

MINE COUNTERMEASURES SHIPS (MCMV)
HUNT CLASS

Ship	Pennant Number	Completion Date	Builder
LEDBURY	M30	1981	Vosper T
CATTISTOCK	M31	1982	Vosper T
BROCKLESBY	M33	1983	Vosper T
MIDDLETON	M34	1984	Yarrow
CHIDDINGFOLD	M37	1984	Vosper T
HURWORTH	M39	1985	Vosper T

Displacement: 750 tonnes FL **Dimensions:** 60m x 10.5m x 3.4m **Machinery:** 2 Caterpillar C32 ACERT diesels; 1 Deltic 9-55B diesel for pulse generator and auxiliary drive; 2 shafts; 1 bow thruster **Speed:** 15 knots **Armament:** 1 x 30mm; 2 x Miniguns **Complement:** 45 crew and 5 officers

Notes: With the introduction of new autonomous methods of dealing with the threat posed by sea mines, the future for the mine countermeasures vessels of the Hunt Class would seem, on paper to be limited. Under current plans, over the next few years the oldest members of the class will be retired from service and replaced with autonomous systems that can be remotely operated from a wide variety of naval vessels from a safe distance removing the danger to life posed by these weapons.

LEDBURY, the oldest member of the fleet, entered service as long ago as 1980 but regular retrofits have enabled the ship to remain current when faced with an increasingly technologically advanced threat that is becoming more deadly and harder to combat with each successive year. Refits often include improved diesel generators, along with upgraded hull and crew accommodation. During a refit the team at BAE Systems completes over 65,000 production hours on each MCMV including a full structural re-baselining of the ship with over two miles of laminating cloth being laid, extensive system enhancements undertaken, as well as maintenance and defect rectification.

Two members of the class, CHIDDINGFOLD and BROCKLESBY, are forward deployed to the Persian Gulf to provide a permanent Royal Navy presence together with two Sandown-class minehunters as part of Operation Kipion. The four MCMVs use highly trained Mine Clearance Divers and the SeaFox unmanned mine disposal system to detect and neutralise mines.

The Hunt Class will be replaced in service by new autonomous mine-warfare vessels that are cheaper and more expendable than manned vessels. The Royal Navy is collaborating with their French counterparts in the development of a £117million Maritime Mine Counter Measures (MMCM). It is expected that the last of the Hunt Class will leave service by 2031.

CROWN COPYRIGHT/MOD **HMS Cattistock**

HMS Grimsby

MINE COUNTERMEASURES SHIPS
SANDOWN CLASS

Ship	Pennant Number	Completion Date	Builder
PENZANCE	M106	1998	Vosper T
PEMBROKE	M107	1998	Vosper T
GRIMSBY	M108	1999	Vosper T
BANGOR	M109	2000	Vosper T
SHOREHAM	M112	2001	Vosper T

Displacement: 600 tonnes **Dimensions:** 52.5m x 10.9m x 2.3m **Machinery:** 2 Paxman Valenta diesels, 1,523 hp; Voith-Schneider propulsion; 2 bow thrusters **Speed:** 13 knots **Armament:** 1 x 30mm gun; 2 x Miniguns; 3 x GPMG **Complement:** 34

Notes: The Sandown-class Mine Counter Measure Vessels are based in Scotland. The staff and ships of Mine Counter Measures 1 (MCM1) Squadron deploy in the Northern Gulf, conduct NATO exercises with other nations and work around the British Coastline, protecting the United Kingdom's shores and clearing the old ordnance that remains as a legacy of previous wars. These five surviving Sandown-class vessels are to be gradually replaced in service by new unmanned autonomous mine disposal systems by 2025. The Sandown Class will be retired before the more capable Hunt-class vessels. These ships are still comparatively young, and it is very likely that they will be sold abroad for further service. At the end of August 2021, after a three-year deployment in the Arabian Gulf, SHOREHAM and Hunt-class BROCKLESBURY, returned back to the UK. Both MCMVs started much needed refits in Faslane and Portsmouth before they returned to fleet service in 2022. Their Gulf duties were taken over by BANGOR and MIDDLETON.

MINE HUNTING DRONE (MMCM)

Displacement: N/A **Dimensions:** N/A **Payload:** N/A **Speed:** N/A **Complement:** cabin for crew but usually unmanned

Notes: The first drone was handed over to the Royal Navy for evaluation and trials in late 2021 under a Franco British project known in France as SLAM-F and in the United Kingdom as MMCM. The agreement between the two countries was agreed as part of the Lancaster House military agreement (2010). France and Great Britain and to a lesser extent the likes of the Netherlands and Belgium have a very similar geographical requirement for replacement minesweeping and mine-hunting capabilities and also share the same problem of rapidly ageing fleets of legacy mine-warfare vessels. The contract for the design and development of a single drone for both France and Britain was ratified in 2015 with Thales and OCCAR on behalf of the two countries.

The MMCM system comprises two USVs (one of which is fitted with a towed sonar) and the other a remotely operated robot (ROV), and two UAVs. These systems together are tasked with the detection of, classifying of and locating of sea mines in coastal and littoral waters. The ROV will be used to neutralise the threat posed by the mines.

Crucial to MMCM is the elimination, as much as possible, of humans in the area of greatest danger. Furthermore, with the use of robotics it will be possible to dive deeper, up to 300 metres, and destroy more weapons more efficiently.

The demonstrator was officially handed over to the Royal Navy in Plymouth on 23 November 2021 by staff from Thales UK, OCCAR and Defence Equipment and Support (DE&S), the procurement arm of the UK Ministry of Defence.

The three vessels have been given the names ARTEMIS, APOLLO and ABDIEL.

MARITIME MINE COUNTERMEASURES SYSTEMS (MMCS)

Displacement: 6,000 kg **Dimensions:** 11m x 3.2m x 0.5m **Payload:** 4 tonnes **Speed:** 40+ knots
Complement: cabin for crew but usually unmanned

Notes: On 20 January 2021, the MoD awarded Atlas Elektronik UK a £25 million contract to deliver Great Britain's first MHC Block 1 unmanned minesweeper. Two further vessels have been delivered against the contract that utilises autonomous, more expendable vessels against the deadly threat posed by sea mines.

HEBE, named after the ancient Greek goddess of youth, joined sister vessels HARRIER and HAZARD as part of the Royal Navy's crewless mine-hunting programme Project 'Wilton'. HEBE has an extended cabin with more technology on board and is four metres longer than her sisters.

The vessels use a system of cutting-edge technologies known as a 'Combined Influence Sweep' which has been developed to combat modern digital sea mines that are more sophisticated than their pressure, acoustic and contact system predecessors. The uncrewed boats will tow innovative Coiled Auxiliary Boats (CABs) which are made from a novel 'Drop Stitch' inflatable panel material. Onboard the CABs are systems which can generate a variety of simulated signal influences to initiate the mine harmlessly away from ships. The system is controlled remotely at a safe distance on a nearby ship or even many miles away on land.

In December 2021, the MoD announced plans for the future acquisition of further elements of MHC programme that will see two of the three original units operating in United Kingdom waters, based at Portsmouth and Faslane, with the third deployed to the Gulf, probably from the dedicated in-theatre RFA Landing Ship Dock. The system is readily deployable from shore, Royal Navy, RFA or even commercial vessels. Each mission system consists of a Portable Operations Centre, an Autonomous Surface Vessel, towed sonar, mine neutralisation system, autonomous underwater vehicles and an autonomous mine sweeping system.

Block II will comprise of a larger, as yet unspecified, number of MHC Mission Systems that will make up the bulk of the replacement units to replace the Sandown Class by 2025. The investment decision point is currently planned for some time in 2024.

As the Royal Navy has decided to gradually move to autonomous minewarfare technology, we will see minewarfare experts from Sandown-class vessels being re-trained to operate the new autonomous minehunters and their associated state-of-the-art hunting and sweeping equipment. Controlled remotely these autonomous minehunters can be used to detect and classify mines or ordnance dumped in the sea at speed, without putting sailors and a multi-million-pound warship in danger.

CROWN COPYRIGHT/MOD

HMS Spey

PATROL VESSELS
RIVER II CLASS

Ship	Pennant Number	Completion Date	Builder
FORTH	P222	2018	BAE Systems
MEDWAY	P223	2019	BAE Systems
TRENT	P224	2019	BAE Systems
TAMAR	P233	2019	BAE Systems
SPEY	P234	2019	BAE Systems

Displacement: 2,000 tonnes **Dimensions:** 90.5m x 13.5m x 3.8m **Speed:** 24 knots
Armament: 1 x 30mm cannon; 2 x Miniguns, 2 x GPMG **Aviation:** Flight deck capable of receiving aircraft up to Merlin size **Complement:** 36 (accommodation for 70)

Notes: The River II Class were developed from the previous River Class but are significantly more advanced and larger vessels with far greater capabilities including the addition of a flight deck capable of accommodating a Merlin helicopter; a capability that has been evaluated on MEDWAY during her current Caribbean deployment.

Each of the River IIs feature enhanced firefighting equipment, BAEs CMS-1 combat management system, an I Band Doppler SharpEye radar for helicopter control and improved accommodation. In fact, the bridge of a River II-class patrol vessel compares extremely favourably against a Type 45 destroyer or Type 23 frigate with plenty of space for personnel. Each of the five River II class ships have been painted in traditional dazzle colour schemes reminiscent of World War convoy escorts.

TAMAR and SPEY are deployed to the Pacific providing a constant RN presence in the region, although without any permanent shore facilities being made available for the two ships. They will instead victual at ports of opportunity and at naval bases of allies and friendly nations. MEDWAY continues to operate in the Caribbean providing a permanent presence in that region.

FORTH remains in service as the dedicated Falkland Islands Guardship and TRENT in the Mediterranean where she spent a large portion of 2022 conducting flying trials with helicopters and dedicated QinetiQ flight test engineers from MoD Boscombe Down.

CROWN COPYRIGHT/MOD   **HMS Tamar**

● DEREK FOX   **HMS Severn**

PATROL VESSELS
RIVER CLASS

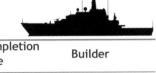

Ship	Pennant Number	Completion Date	Builder
TYNE	P281	2002	Vosper T
SEVERN	P282	2003	Vosper T
MERSEY	P283	2003	Vosper T

Displacement: 1,677 tonnes **Dimensions:** 79.5m x 13.6m x 3.8m **Machinery:** 2 MAN 12RK 270 diesels, 11,063 hp; 2 shafts; bow thruster **Speed:** 20+ knots **Armament:** 1 x 20mm; 2 x GPMG **Complement:** 48

Notes: These three ships were originally ordered from Vosper Thornycroft in 2001 on a then unusual deal whereby the Royal Navy leased them from the shipbuilder for five years at a cost of £60 million. A £52 million lease extension was agreed in January 2007 running to the end of 2013. The Ministry of Defence in 2012 authorised the purchase of the three ships from the shipbuilder for the price of £39 million.

The MoD intended to keep them operational for another ten years through to 2022. For a while it was expected that the new RIVER II-class would replace them in service and SEVERN was decommissioned in October 2017, but with the current Government's foreign policy statement on having dispersed naval assets around the globe, the RIVER IIs have been forward deployed leaving their older, smaller, and less capable, sister ships to maintain the round the clock protection of Great Britain's borders and vital Fishery Protection Role.

In November 2018, it was announced that the future of these three ships was secure for some time, but their future, or any replacements, other than the five RIVER IIs are unclear at the present time.

MERSEY, TYNE and SEVERN have a wide variety of taskings including escorting foreign warships passing through UK waters, conducting fishing vessel inspections and defending the UK border. Increasingly, they have also been used during the current illegal immigrant crisis in the English Channel.

The vessels also have an unique role in providing training for navigators from 700X Naval Air Squadron, who use the ships for testing their latest remotely-piloted Puma air system. With a range beyond 10 miles and an endurance of more than two hours, the Puma can vastly increase the ability of a ship to gather intelligence. Flying up to 45 miles per hour, the drones combine a high-tech control system with their array of sensors, including a times-fifty optical zoom, to live-stream video back to the ship. 700X Naval Air Squadron conducts its own training programme to prepare personnel for the Puma flights. The squadron also teaches military personnel from across defence in the use of quadcopters. It also researches and evaluates a wide range of remotely-piloted systems as the sector continues to increase.

● CROWN COPYRIGHT/MOD   **Puma Air System**

HMS Ranger

COASTAL TRAINING CRAFT
P2000 CLASS

Ship	Pennant Number	Completion Date	Builder
EXPRESS	P163	1988	Vosper T
EXPLORER	P164	1985	Watercraft
EXAMPLE	P165	1985	Watercraft
EXPLOIT	P167	1988	Vosper T
ARCHER	P264	1985	Watercraft
BITER	P270	1985	Watercraft
SMITER	P272	1986	Watercraft
PURSUER	P273	1988	Vosper T
TRACKER	P274	1998	Ailsa Troon
RAIDER	P275	1998	Ailsa Troon
BLAZER	P279	1988	Vosper T
DASHER	P280	1988	Vosper T

Ship	Pennant Number	Completion Date	Builder
PUNCHER	P291	1988	Vosper T
CHARGER	P292	1988	Vosper T
RANGER	P293	1988	Vosper T
TRUMPETER	P294	1988	Vosper T

Displacement: 54 tonnes Dimensions: 20.8m x 5.8m x 1.8m Machinery: 2 Caterpillar C18 diesels, 1,746 hp; 2 MTU diesels, 2,000 hp (TRACKER); 2 shafts Speed: 20 knots Armament: 3 x GPMG (Faslane-based vessels) Complement: 5 (with accommodation for up to 12).

Notes: These fourteen vessels are among the oldest Royal Navy units dating from the mid-1980s, but there are currently no plans for their replacement. Their role is to train future command personnel and most of the class are attached to University Royal Naval Units (URNU) but can also contribute to numerous other naval tasks around the waters of the United Kingdom and into European waters.

Vessels are assigned to the following URNUs, ARCHER (East Scotland); BITER (Manchester & Salford), BLAZER (Southampton); CHARGER (Liverpool); EXAMPLE (Northumbria); EXPLOIT (Birmingham); EXPLORER (Yorkshire); EXPRESS (Wales); PUNCHER (London); RANGER (Sussex); SMITER (Oxford); TRUMPETER (Cambridge).

RANGER and TRUMPETER were formerly allocated to the Gibraltar Squadron for guard ship and search and rescue duties, but were replaced by the dedicated Scimitar-class patrol boats. Unlike the remainder of the class, both these ships remain capable of being mounted with a 20mm cannon. In 2020, DASHER and PURSUER replaced the Scimitar-class SCIMITAR and SABRE as the Gibraltar Squadron.

SCIMITAR and SABRE were shipped back to the United Kingdom where they supplemented the training role performed by the ARCHER P2000 boats with University Royal Naval Units. They have been removed from service and were sold in September 2022. In 2021, DASHER and PURSUER were replaced by the new Gibraltar Fast Patrol Boats (see following page) constructed on Merseyside by Marine Specialist Technology.

● DANIEL FERRO

HMS Dagger (left) and HMS Cutlass

GIBRALTAR SQUADRON
FAST PATROL BOATS

Ship	Pennant Number	Completion Date	Builder
CUTLASS	P295	2021	Marine Specialised Tech
DAGGER	P296	2022	Marine Specialised Tech

Displacemen:t 35 tonnes Dimensions: 19m in length Machinery: 3x Volvo D13-1000 engines driving 3x MJP350X waterjets Speed: up to 40+ knots Armament: 3 x General Purpose Machine Guns (fitted for but not with 0.50cal Heavy Machine Gun) Complement: 6

Notes: These two vessels are the replacements for SCIMITAR and SABRE. In July 2020, the Ministry of Defence contracted Merseyside-based boat builder Marine Specialised Technology (MTS) to build a pair of new boats for the Gibraltar Squadron in a deal worth £9 million. Both boats are used to patrol HMNB Gibraltar and British Gibraltar Territorial Waters (BGTW) as well as supporting British exercises and operations in the area, keeping a close watch over Gibraltar's shores.

The first vessel - HMS CUTLASS - arrived at Gibraltar on board the general cargo ship DEO VOLENTE on 15 November 2021. DAGGER joined her in April 2022, after a host of sea trials and safety checks, before being able to fly the White Ensign. The trials were completed in the middle of 2022.

The Gibraltar Squadron also operates a trio of Rigid Hull Inflatable Boats (RHIBs) and the recently allocated River II-class patrol ship TRENT.

HMS Scott

SURVEY SHIPS
SCOTT CLASS

Ship	Pennant Number	Completion Date	Builder
SCOTT	H131	1997	Appledore

Displacement: 13,500 tonnes   Dimensions: 131.5m x 21.5m x 8.3m   Machinery: 2 Krupp MaK 9M32 diesels, 10,800 hp; 1 shaft, CP propellor; retractable bow thruster Speed: 17 knots   Complement: 78

Notes: SCOTT is nearing the end of her Royal Navy career having first commissioned in 1997. She was built to commercial standards and continues to provide extremely accurate and detailed deep bathymetric surveys of the continental shelf. She is fitted with modern multi-beam sonar suite with which she can conduct ocean mapping operations on a global scale. Her 78 crewmembers operate a three-watch system whereby the ship is run by 48 of her crew with the remainder on leave at any given time. Each person aboard works 75 days on the ship before having 30 days ashore. In this way SCOTT can remain at sea for more than 300 days a year consolidating the work she has undertaken and avoiding unnecessary wasteful breaks in the surveying. She can navigate through thin Ice Class 1A conditions but only with the assistance of a dedicated icebreaker.

SCOTT is the largest survey vessel in Western Europe, and the fifth largest vessel in the Royal Navy. Named for the famous Arctic explorer Robert Falcon Scott, she also has an auxiliary role as a mine countermeasures vessel. In her 24 years at sea, the ship has surveyed approximately 3.7 per cent of the world's oceans alone - impressive when you consider that only one fifth of the world's oceans have been surveyed to modern standards.

Following a multi-million refit at Falmouth SCOTT sailed on a 15-month deployment in July 2022.

Out of service date for SCOTT has been set as 2023 but this may be extended. There will be no immediate direct replacement for this vessel or her capabilities. Her replacement is officially 'under consideration' at present but is closely tied to the procurement of the Multi-Role Ocean Surveillance Ship (MROSS) that was promised in the 2021 Integrated Review. The primary role of the MROSS is to be the protection of undersea communication cables and other infrastructure vital to the security and prosperity of the United Kingdom. The role of the MROSS is similar but not identical to that of SCOTT due to the numerous multi-beam echo sounders installed, but there are compromises to be made to secure the MROSS programme and an eventual replacement for the survey ship, although there will be a period where the Royal Navy's survey fleet will consist of just ENTERPRISE and the tiny MAGPIE.

CROWN COPYRIGHT/MOD

HMS Scott

● GORDON BRODIE

HMS Enterprise

ECHO CLASS

Ship	Pennant Number	Completion Date	Builder
ENTERPRISE	H88	2003	Appledore

Displacement: 3,500 tonnes Dimensions: 90.6m x 16.8m x 5.5.m Machinery: Diesel electric; 3 DG (4.8MW); 2 x azimuth thrusters, 2,279 hp (1.7 MW); 1 bow thruster Speed: 15 knots Armament: 2 x 20mm Complement: 48 (with accommodation for 81)

Notes: ENTERPRISE is a multi-role survey vessel – hydrographic oceanographic (SVHO) and together with her (decommissioned) sister ship ECHO form the Echo-class survey ships. The two ships were built in Devon at Appledore Shipbuilders who had been subcontracted by prime contractors Vosper Thornycroft to build the ships. Their role is primarily one of survey and oceanographic research although they retain a secondary role as mine countermeasures HQ ships. Of the crew of 72 on each ship only about 48 are ever aboard with the remainder on leave, training, or other duties.

In May 2022, ECHO was reduced to low readiness/reserve status. On 30 June 2022, she was decommissioned at Portsmouth Naval Base, while ENTERPRISE's 20-year Royal Navy career will formally end at the end of March 2023.

ENTERPRISE and ECHO are being replaced by the Navy's Future Military Data Gathering Programme being introduced over the next 18 months, deploying specialist teams with state-of-the-art equipment, including drones and autonomous systems, on other vessels – including commercial ships – to gather the relevant information.

CROWN COPYRIGHT/MOD

HMS Protector

ICE PATROL SHIP PROTECTOR

Ship	Pennant Number	Completion Date	Builder
PROTECTOR	A173	2001	Havyard Leirvik (Norway)

Displacement: 4,985 tonnes **Dimensions:** 89.7m x 18m x 7.25m **Machinery:** 2 Rolls Royce Bergen diesels, 9,602 hp; 1 shaft; CP propellor; bow and stern thrusters **Speed:** 15 knots **Armament:** Miniguns; GPMGs **Complement:** 88 (accommodation for up to 100)

Notes: PROTECTOR is the Royal Navy's only Ice Patrol Ship and is usually found operating in the freezing waters of Antarctica and the Southern Hemisphere. PROTECTOR's ship's company includes a team of permanent divers who undertake exploratory surveys. The vessel spent five-months in dry dock in Teeside in 2020 being extensively overhauled and upgraded including the creation of a new quarterdeck structure with a naval stores complex, new workshops to maintain the ship's two small survey craft JAMES CAIRD IV and the 8.5m Rigid Work Boat TERRA NOVA.

As Britain's dedicated Ice Patrol Ship PROTECTOR is usually found in the Southern Oceans, but the impact of global warming on the planet is having an arguably greater impact in the Arctic and in 2022 the ship visited northern polar regions for the second time in two years to conduct scientific experiments and to chart the loss of the ice cap as the planet warms. As part of this mission the ship has worked with drone experts from 700X Squadron from Culdrose to equip PROTECTOR with 'eyes in the sky' in the form of Evolve Dynamics' Sky Mantis drones. These aircraft can be used to identify areas of ice concentration and 'leads' – gaps in the ice through which she can safely navigate. The drones can also assist with aerial scientific survey work.

HMS Magpie

INSHORE SURVEY VESSEL

Ship	Pennant Number	Completion Date	Builder
MAGPIE	H130	2018	Safehaven

Displacement: 37 tonnes Dimensions: 18m x 6.2m x 1.4m Machinery: 2x Volvo D16 diesels, 524 hp; 2 shafts Speed: 23 knots Complement: 12

Notes: MAGPIE replaced GLEANER in 2018 and has since then been actively surveying the inshore waters around the United Kingdom. She was purchased as one of 38 new workboats supplied by Atlas Elektronik and is unique in having a catamaran hull. She can operate offshore for up to 7 days with a crew of 12 and has a range of 1,400 nautical miles.

One of MAGPIE's first major taskings after commissioning in June 2018 was a continuation of work done by her predecessor GLEANER in surveying Portsmouth Harbour to ensure the stability of the seabed in anticipation of Portsmouth's use by the aircraft carriers QUEEN ELIZABETH and PRINCE OF WALES.

In March 2020 she was extensively updated with new software and electronics to keep her at the forefront of surveying technology. In 2022 the diminutive MAGPIE conducted a three-month survey of the River Tyne before sailing north to Scotland for a series of extensive surveys. She will also play a key role in the development of future capability by testing remote and autonomous systems along with other techniques to better collect and exploit environmental data.

Patrick Blackett

NAVYX SUPPORT VESSEL

Ship	Pennant Number	Completion Date	Builder
PATRICK BLACKETT	X01	2022	Damen Group

Displacement: 270 tonnes **Dimensions:** 41.2m x 8.7m x 3m **Machinery:** 4 x Caterpillar C32 Ascert diesel engines **Speed:** 23 knots **Armament:** None **Complement:** 5

Notes: This unique £9 million adapted Fast Crew Supplier 4008 (FCS 4008), designed and built by Damen Group, was acquired by the Royal Navy to test and evaluate state-of-the-art modern technologies, particularly autonomous systems as they are developed for maritime use. The steel hulled/aluminium superstructure vessel was purchased under the NavyX programme.

She has been equipped to operate the Royal Navy's PODS (Persistently Operationally Deployed System) which is located on the large cargo deck of the ship. She will also be infinitely adaptable for specific trials and experiments be they underwater, surface or aerial in nature. Some tests will be less visible to the casual observer as it is expected that she will also evaluate Artificial Intelligence warfighting solutions. She is named after the British physicist and Noble Prize winner Patrick Blackett, who made a major contribution in World War Two advising on military strategy and developing operational research.

She is painted matt black, rather than the Royal Navy's standard Pusser's Grey, complete with NavyX insignia on both sides of the hull. Her pennant, X01, is also uniquely highlighted in gloss paint and large QR codes are painted to either side of her superstructure, allowing smartphone users to scan them and view NavyX content.

Madfox

NAVYX MADFOX
UNMANNED SURFACE VESSEL

MADFOX standing for Maritime Demonstrator For Operational eXperimentation, was accepted into the Royal Navy in 2021 after being evaluated by the Defence Science and Technology Laboratory (Dstl) over a period of eighteen months. Based on the L3Harris Mast-13 autonomous vessel, MADFOX will be further evaluated by the Royal Navy in a variety of real-life scenarios to examine how autonomous vessels can deliver force multipliers, force protection and surveillance and reconnaissance assets to the fleet. For this next phase in its assessment process the vessel will be under the control of the NavyX organisation that is tasked with evaluating new and innovative pieces of equipment for the Royal Navy. NAVYX is also currently evaluating an autonomous Rigid Inflatable Boat (RIB) that will be incorporated into the inventory of the future Type 26 and Type 31 frigates.

Madfox

Royal Marine Craft

The first records of Royal Marines were founded by King Charles II on 28 October 1664, but it wasn't until 1802 that they were given the name Royal Marines by King George III. In those 359 years the RM has earned a reputation for supreme bravery and excellence which continues to this day.

2021 saw a radical transformation of the force's structure, role and uniforms as it transformed into The Future Commando Force (FCF). The process saw the injection of £40 million into the Royal Marines and British amphibious capabilities. The Future Commando Force is swift, agile, and nimble and able to deploy rapidly around the globe at short notice. They are equipped with unique 'game changing' technology, weaponry and equipment unlike that used in any other units in the British armed forces and be capable of undertaking roles ranging from humanitarian aid, combat missions to full-scale warfighting. They will regularly deploy on attachment to the UKs' Carrier Strike Groups but also be retained in home waters. In July 2020, the Royal Marines created The Vanguard Strike Company, a unit of more than 150 Marines and British Army Commandos. But, some things are unchanged, including the spiritual home of the Commandos at Plymouth even if the FCFs' focus will increasingly become one of technical specialist operations.

To achieve the aim of increased agility personnel will work in 'small, versatile teams' specially tailored for each individual mission. Each Marine will be specially selected by individual skill sets allowing more autonomy of movement and decision at the company level. This could be as small as teams of four as was tested by 40 Commando in 2020 at Bovington Training Area in Dorset.

The Government's focus on forward deploying British forces abroad also applies to the Future Commando Force, with the aim of establishing high readiness groups in warships and auxiliaries already on deployment.

The Royal Marines will continue to operate landing craft from the assault ships BULWARK and ALBION and the Bay-class landing ships. Furthermore, they have a range of small fast inshore boats and assault craft on which Royal Marine personnel are trained at Plymouth, Instow in North Devon and at HMS Raleigh at Torpoint. The latter location houses the Royal Navy School of Board and Search, which trains personnel in the special skills of boarding vessels underway that may restrict searches.

The Royal Navy has 15 Reserve Units and a Fleet Diving Squadron consisting of 10 Units. The Royal Marines consists of 3 Commando Brigade, the Royal Marine Band Service, the Commando Training Centre and 4 Reserve Units.

ISLAND CLASS PATROL VESSELS

Ship	Pennant Number	Launch Date	Builder
RONA	-	2009	Holyhead Marine
MULL	-	2010	Holyhead Marine
EORSA	-	2014	Holyhead Marine

Displacement: 19.9 tonnes   Dimensions: 14.9m x 4.6m x 0.9m   Machinery: 2 Caterpillar diesels, 715 hp; 2 waterjets   Speed: 33 knots   Armament: 4 x GPMG   Complement: 3

Notes: The Island-class patrol boats RONA and MULL were former Ministry of Defence Police vessels from the Clyde Marine Unit at HMNB Clyde, handed over to the Royal Marines in 2013. They were fitted with three new weapons mounts, extra protection and communications equipment and transferred to 43 Commando Fleet Protection Group Royal Marines for operation on the Clyde to escort high value units such as the Vanguard-class submarines. A third vessel, EORSA, was delivered direct from the builders. (An Island-class patrol vessel is pictured on the left in the photograph).

LCU Mk10

Ship	Pennant Number	Parent Unit	Builder
9730	1001	47 CRGRM	Ailsa, Troon
9731	1002	47 CRGRM	Ailsa, Troon
9732	1003	HMS ALBION	BAE Systems
9733	1004	HMS ALBION	BAE Systems
9734	1005	HMS ALBION	BAE Systems
9735	1006	HMS ALBION	BAE Systems
9736	1007	47 CRGRM	BAE Systems
9737	1008	47 CRGRM	BAE Systems
9738	1009	47 CRGRM	BAE Systems
9739	1010	47 CRGRM	BAE Systems

Displacement: 240 tonnes Dimensions: 29.82m x 7.7m x 1.70m Machinery: 2 MAN Diesels; 2 Schottel propulsors; 1 bow thruster Speed: 10 knots Armament: 2 x GPMG Complement: 7

Notes: LCU Mk10 (Landing Craft Utility) are operated by the Royal Marines and are a Ro-Ro style landing craft designed to operate from Albion-class LPDs or Landing Ship Dock Auxiliary (LSDA). Ordered in 1998 from Ailsa Troon, the fleet currently consists of ten vessels, with the first two delivered in 1999 and with the final vessels being accepted into service in 2003. The remainder were built by BAE Systems at Govan. Both ALBION and BULWARK are each capable of carrying four LCUs.

They have a 'drive-through' configuration, with ramps fore and aft and pilot house shifted to starboard. They are capable of transporting up to 120 fully equipped troops, one main battle tank or four large vehicles. With a range of around 600 nautical miles – more if auxiliary tanks are added – they are designed to operate independently for 14 days with a seven man Royal Marine crew in both arctic and tropical climates. All the crew members have bunk accommodation and there is a galley and store rooms.

● CROWN COPYRIGHT/MOD   Mexeflote

Mexeflote
Dimensions: 38.66m x 12.4m x 1.54m **Speed:** 6.5 knots **Complement:** 6 Crew

Notes: The Mexeflote consists of multiple cells and engines that can be configured to provide a causeway, landing craft or Ramp Support Pontoon. It is capable of transferring vehicles and equipment up to 198 tonnes and is routinely deployed worldwide via LSDs of the Royal Fleet Auxiliary. The Mexeflote is the largest logistic landing craft in the military and is operated exclusively by the Royal Logistic Corps. The Mexeflote is highly versatile and has been deployed in support of the majority of operational deployments since the Falklands conflict.

Landing Craft Vehicle and Personnel (LCVP)

LCVP Mk5B

Ship	Pennant Number	Parent Unit	Builder
0202	B5	47 CRGRM	Babcock Marine
0203	NM	HMS ALBION	Babcock Marine
0204	B6	47 CRGRM	Babcock Marine
0205	P7	47 CRGRM	Babcock Marine
0338	T6	47 CRGRM	Babcock Marine
0339		HMS ALBION	Babcock Marine
0340	N2	HMS ALBION	Babcock Marine
0341	P9	47 CRGRM	Babcock Marine
0344		47 CRGRM	Babcock Marine
0345		47 CRGRM	Babcock Marine
0346	N3	HMS ALBION	Babcock Marine
0347		47 CRGRM	Babcock Marine
0353		47 CRGRM	Babcock Marine

Ship	Pennant Number	Parent Unit	Builder
0354		47 CRGRM	Babcock Marine
0355		47 CRGRM	Babcock Marine
0356	B8	47 CRGRM	Babcock Marine

Displacement: 24 tonnes Dimensions: 15.70m x 4.2m x 0.90m Machinery: 2 Volvo Penta diesels; 2 waterjets Speed: 25 knots Armament: 2 x GPMG Complement: 3

Notes: Designed to carry personnel and small vehicles, the first LCVP Mk5 (Landing Craft Vehicle and Personnel) was ordered in 1995 from Vosper Thornycroft and handed over in 1996. A further four were delivered in December 1996 with two more for training at RM Poole ordered in 1998. A further 16 were ordered from FBM Babcock Marine in 2001 with the final vessels being accepted into service in 2004. The Mk 5 can transport 8 tonnes of stores or a mix of 2 tonnes and 35 fully equipped troops, and operate from both ALBION and BULWARK. These vessels represent a significant improvement in capability over the preceding Mk4s with a greater range, lift and speed. They feature aluminium hulls and are powered by twin waterjets. Their design includes a rigid and enclosed windowed canopy and a ramp at the bow that lowers for rapid unloading. GPMGs can be mounted when needed. The primary role is the landing of vehicles, personnel and equipment onto potentially hostile shores. The secondary role is a general purpose support craft both between ships and ship to shore. The craft are capable of performing normal duties in conditions up to sea state 4 and run for cover up to sea state 5. Pennant numbers and parent units can change as the vessels are rotated through maintenance cycles.

Landing Craft Vehicle and Personnel (LCVP)

OFFSHORE RAIDING CRAFT (ORC)

Weight: 3.6 tonnes **Dimensions:** 9.1m x 2.9m x 0.66m **Machinery:** Twin Steyr MO256K43 250 bhp @ 4200rpm **Propulsion:** Rolls Royce FF270 Waterjets **Speed:** 36 knots **Armament:** 1x HMG/GPMG forward, 2 x GPMG/HMG/GMG/Minigun aft **Complement:** 2 and 8 troops

Notes: The Royal Marines operate two versions of the Offshore Raiding Craft (ORC), the Troop Carrying Variant (TCV) and Fire Support Variant (FSV). The ORC is an air portable surface manoeuvre craft designed for the rapid deployment of 8 fully equipped troops and 2 crew from over the horizon (30 miles) ship-to-shore and vice versa. They provide rapid movement of troops in coastal, estuarine, riverine and inland waters. The ORC has an aluminium hull with a low draught to allow for safe, rapid beach insertions. To provide ballistic protection for her 2 crew and passengers optional armour panels can be fitted.She can be transported as under-slung load by Chinook and Merlin helicopters or air-transported inside a C130 Hercules transport plane. Around 39 ORCs are in service with the Royal Marines. The ORC is manufactured by Holyhead Marine of Anglesey, North Wales.

RIGID RAIDING CRAFT

Notes: The Royal Marines operate a large number of smaller Rigid-hulled and Rigid-Inflatable Craft for various assault, patrol and security duties. There are 5.2, 6.5 and 8 metre long versions. Rigid Raiders feature GRP (glass reinforced plastic) hulls and early variants featured single or twin outboard motors. A small team of men can carry the boats, even with engines attached, due to their lightweight construction. They can also be air-dropped out to sea. The latest RRC, the Mk3, is powered by a 240 hp inboard diesel engine but the Royal Marines might start replacing these with ORCs. They can carry up to eight troops. Rigid Raiders are manufactured by RTK Marine (now part of BAE Systems).

SPECIALIST CRAFT

In addition to the familiar Rigid Raiding Craft and Rigid Inflatable Boats other specialist vessels are available including the Fast Interceptor Craft (FIC) with a top speed of 60 knots. Back in July 2007 it was revealed that the Special Boat Service (SBS) were to take delivery of the so-called 'stealth boat'. The vessel is manufactured by Portsmouth-based VT Halmatic, which is now part of BAE Systems, but not much has been revealed about the vessel. The vessel has been spotted numerous times in waters off Poole, home of the SBS, and according to the BAE Systems Maritime website they are currently in service with UK Special Forces.

To maintain a low radar cross-section, external fittings such as raydomes, aerial fits and apertures on the craft are kept to a minimum. This results in low radar and heat signatures enabling a stealth capability. The specification of the boats in service with the UK Special Forces remain a mystery as there are numerous options not only for the propulsion lines (such as twin or triple petrol outboards through to twin diesel stern drives, twin diesel jet drives or twin Arneson surface drives) but also for the system facilities. Options include multiple fuel tank arrangements, water separator/primary filter within the engine compartment, electric and manual bilge systems with automatic sensing and high bilge alarms, fire and/or smoke detection system with visual/audible display on console and/or cabin, variety of navigation and communication systems available to end user specification, including, but not limited to, fully integrated intercom systems, radar, satcom and multiple radio installation.

All craft are air transportable with special trailers available to suit different aircraft including A400M, C130 and C17.

Three models are available 30, 40 and 180.
Dimensions - Model 30: 10.75m x 2.59m x 0.7m
Dimensions - Model 40: 13.07m x 2.83m x 0.82m
Dimensions - Model 180: 18.1m x 3.8m x 0.9m

SWIMMER DELIVERY VEHICLES

Swimmer Delivery Vehicles (SDV) are miniature submarines operated by Britain's Special Forces to insert commandos and others into frontline situations or to undertake clandestine work. The Royal Navy owns three SDV Mk8 Mod 1 versions which are used by the Special Boat Service.

The Mk8 is the same vehicle used by the United States Navy SEAL teams, although the SEALs are upgrading their SDVs with the Shallow Water Combat Submersible (SWCS), designated as the Mk 11 SDV. In 2018 the UK government announced the intention to purchase three replacement SWCS for their existing fleet of SDVs.

On January 14, 2021, the US Department of Defense announced that a foreign military sale request from Teledyne Brown Engineering, the manufacturers of the SWCS, for around USD39 million firm-fixed price modification to an existing contract had been awarded. The buyer nation was not disclosed due to the secretive nature of the technology involved but is widely believed to be to honour the British contract.

Ships for the Future Fleet

TYPE 32

First announced on 19 November 2020 as part of a defence investment pledge prior to the Integrated Review. Whereas the Type 26 frigates will make up the high end of the technological mainstream of the fleet, Type 32s would be designed primarily to act in defence of the territorial or littoral waters around Great Britain and provide 'persistent presence' in support of the new Littoral Response Groups (LRGs).

Much of the design work on the Type 32 has yet to be completed but what is known is that Defence Minister Ben Wallace envisages these ships to function as a 'platform for autonomous systems' and used in the widest variety of roles from anti-submarine warfare to mine countermeasures activities. They will also share a common heritage with the Type 26 and Type 31e in that they will be of modular design and general purpose in focus with the construction work expected to go to Scottish shipyards.

ASTUTE CLASS SUCCESSOR - SSN(R)

It is something of a truism in defence that you never stand still. Evolve or die. Such is the case with the development of attack submarines. In 2018 the Maritime Underwater Future Capability (MUFC) was established to determine the course of travel for future submarine development after the completion of the Astute-class submarines. The MUFC was begun as an Initial Concept Phase but was almost immediately thereafter suspended for a further two years, most likely driven by the need to focus, time, money and energy into the Dreadnought and overrunning Astute programmes and get both back on track. Any other distractions from these two core projects it was assumed could be mitigated.

The MUFC resurfaced in the Integrated Defence Review and has the new name of SSN(R). With construction of the first of these submarines unlikely to commence much before the late 2030s, this project has a long way to run yet, but already there are some common threads that are likely to be incorporated into the new replacement submarine programme. Stealth technologies, both physical and technological and the growth in the use of unmanned systems will play an increasing part in the design philosophy.

It is extremely likely that the SSN(R) will be up to 25 per cent larger than the Astutes they will replace to allow for the installation of a PWR-3 nuclear reactor, heavier armament and more defensive countermeasures. There is also the possibility that an enlarged 'hangar' for a Chalfont-type DDS may be incorporated into the design. An X tail is another consideration that respected industry analysts suspect are key drivers in the SSN(R)s current design.

A consideration for having larger submarines, however, would be the existing refit facilities at Devonport. The existing dry-docks would need to be extended to take the 25 per cent larger hull.

TYPE 83 DESTROYERS

The integrated Defence Review highlighted the need to lay long-term ambitions to replace the current fleet of Type 45 Air Defence Destroyers in the late 2030 – early 2040 timeframe. Current thinking is to develop a version of the Type 26 frigate to perform this role originally known as the T4X project. 2021's Defence Command Paper stated that the United Kingdom will build a new class of warships with the aim being that 'the concept and assessment phase for our new Type 83 destroyer which will be begin to replace our Type 45 destroyers in the late 2030s'.

The use of a variant of a pre-existing design could prove to be a wise idea as it will cut design and development time and could create a continuous stream of shipbuilding in the United Kingdom for the Royal Navy. If the Royal Navy were to replace the Daring Class with six Type 83s this could see the aim of continuous shipbuilding in Glasgow on the Type 26 production line extending beyond the eight Type 26s already ordered or projected. In February 2022, the MoD announced that the design effort behind the Type 83 destroyer would consider the threat posed by Hypersonic missile systems when designing these new expensive vessels. What these measures are remains uncertain.

FLEET SOLID SUPPORT REPLACEMENT PROGRAMME

On 16 November 2022 Team Resolute, one of the bidders for the construction of three Fleet Solid Support Ships, comprising of BMT, Harland and Wolff and Navantia UK, were appointed as the preferred bidder to deliver these critically required new vessels to the Royal Fleet Auxiliary. The contract worth £1.6 billion will, if exercised, provide a trio of modern supply ships and crucially the majority of the work will be completed within the United Kingdom supporting British shipbuilding.

Spanish-owned Navantia UK will be the prime contractor who will transfer cutting edge digital shipyard knowledge to Harland and Wolff in Belfast. This technology transfer element of Team Resolute's proposal is said to have been one of the deciding factors in awarding the contract to the team. Some components will be manufactured in Spain, but the vast majority will be fabricated in the United Kingdom and final assembly and commissioning will be at Harland and Wolff. Construction of the new ships, based on the British BMT design, will begin as soon as the £77 million investment into Harland and Wolff's shipyard facilities is completed. The pressing need, however, remains that RFA FORT VICTORIA still needs to be replaced by 2028. The other two new ships are expected to enter service by 2032.

NATIONAL YACHT

In November 2022, it was announced that plans to build a new National Flagship, what many refer to as a new 'Royal Yacht', were scrapped. The vessel was going to be named after the late Prince Philip. Secretary of State for Defence Ben Wallace told MPs that he would instead prioritise the procurement of the Multi-Role Ocean Surveillance Ships (MROSS) instead of the flagship.

SUPPORT VESSEL

L ate 2021, the Royal Navy announced a £9 million contract to acquire a vessel suitable to support trials for 'autonomy development'. Autonomous vessels, submarines, aircraft, drones and weapon systems are the buzz words of technological development within all spheres of Royal Navy activity and the procurement of a small 500 tonnes vessel to support in the development and deployment of these systems is a logical one.

The contract specified a vessel of steel construction with a draught not greater than 3.5m, a top speed of 20 knots and a range of 2,500 nautical miles. Crucially the vessel must have a large stern section capable of accommodating a variety of standard 40 foot and 20 foot ISO containers, be fitted with a suitable crane, and be able to tow small boats including RHIBs. It is also likely that the vessel itself will also be autonomous in nature. Navy(X), the department of the Royal Navy leading the development of the future fleet, have stated that they are looking at a small 'Fast Crew Vessel' to serve as a testbed and trials ship.

OCEAN SURVEILLANCE SHIP

O ne of the announcements made in the 2021 Integrated Defence and Security Review was the planned construction of a dedicated Multi Role Ocean Surveillance Ship (MROSS). This vessel will, it is hoped, be delivered to the Royal Navy by 2024 and will provide the fleet with the ability to undertake deep-sea surveillance of the critical undersea communication cables through which virtually all of the world's data and money transactions occur. Any break or sabotage to these vital links could be disastrous. The new ship is expected to have a crew of around 15 and will be able to be deployed globally and particularly in the highly contested Arctic regions to conduct research, survey work and to provide command and control and support services to several smaller manned and unmanned autonomous undersea drones and other vessels currently planned to be joining the fleet over the next decade.

At the Conservative Party Conference in October 2022 Defence Secretary Ben Wallace surprised the audience when he announced that there would be a second Multi-Role Ocean Surveillance Ship ordered for the Royal Navy. He said in light of the mysterious damage inflicted on the Nord Stream pipelines that: "Russia makes no secret of its ability to target such infrastructure, and it's for that reason I can announce we have recently committed to two specialist ships with the capability to keep our cables and pipelines safe. The first multi-role survey ship for seabed warfare will be purchased by the end of this year, fitted out here in the UK and in operation before the end of next year. The second ship will be built in the UK, and we will plan to make sure it covers all our vulnerabilities."

The first vessel RFA PROTEUS has been acquired, whilst a second vessel, to be built, probably in a British shipyard, is in design concept phase. Both ships will be operated by the Royal Fleet Auxiliary.

MILITARY AFLOAT REACH AND SUSTAINABILITY (MARS)

The MARS programme for the replacement of the RFA's Solid Stores Ships rumbles along and still without any clear conclusion in sight. The new ships will replace the positively geriatric 1970s built FORT AUSTIN and FORT ROSALIE and the 1992 built FORT VICTORIA. The new ships will be integrated with the UK Carrier Strike Groups.

Tender documents previously released suggested that each of the three projected ships would be required to have a total cargo capacity of up to 7000sqm, travel at speeds of up to 18 knots without resupply, and be capable of undertaking underway replenishments-at-sea making headway of 12 knots. Each transferable load could weigh up to 5 tonnes and will use the advanced Replenishment-at-Sea Rig (HRAS) developed by Rolls Royce. In November 2018 a shortlist of global shipbuilders was announced only to be halted a year later after several of the bidders dropped out stating it was impossible for them to build the ships and meet the MoD's demanding budget requirements.

In September 2021, the MoD awarded four contender contracts to develop bids to build the Fleet Solid Support vessels. They will be built for the RFA and designed to keep the Queen Elizabeth-class aircraft carriers and amphibious task groups supplied with everything from ammunition to food as they sail on operations around the world. Four contracts worth £5m apiece for the 'Competitive Procurement Phase' have been awarded to develop the design and build of the new ships. The final manufacture contract will be awarded to the UK company acting either solely or as part of a group, following this phase. The next stage will seek details of how they would fulfil the wider delivery needs of the programme. Once this phase is complete, a preferred contender will be selected and a manufacturer contract will be awarded. The four consortia awarded CPP contracts are: Larsen & Toubro, which includes UK company Leidos Innovations; Serco/Damen, which includes UK company Serco; Team Resolute, which includes UK companies Harland & Wolff and BMT; Team UK, which includes UK companies Babcock and BAE Systems.

● BMT TECHNOLOGY

MULTI-ROLE SUPPORT SHIPS (MRSS)

The Ministry of Defence has a stated aim to acquire a small force of Multi-Role Support Ships (MRSS) with the operational role being 'to provide the platforms to deliver Littoral Strike, including Maritime Special Operations, in the early 2030s'. In the past the MoD had wanted to produce two specialist ships - the Littoral Strike Ship (LSS) alongside the new Fleet Solid Support Ships (FSSS) but the former class now appears to have been abandoned. The UK's amphibious and littoral capability at present rests with two Albion-class assault ships and four Bay-class Landing Platform Docks. Both classes are due to be withdrawn by the early 2030s and will need to be replaced. The Royal Navy is following US Navy doctrine closely as it develops both a carrier strike and a littoral strike capability in parallel.

The MRSS programme is intended to provide the Royal Navy and Royal Marines with the ability to transport and deliver troops, vehicles, equipment and supplies anywhere in the world and then support them once in theatre. Such vessels will have a range of specialist capabilities including a large flight deck, replenishment-at-sea capabilities and landing craft.

There is a danger in trying to design the ships to try and achieve too much in one design. Time and again, designers who attempt too much in a single leap forward create white elephants that fail to achieve the desired aims. In general terms the MRSS will be a large, 200 metre long, vessel with large reserves of space for the accommodation of troops, a floodable well deck and a flight deck capable of accommodating the largest military helicopter in British service, the RAF's Boeing Chinook's heavy-lift helicopters.

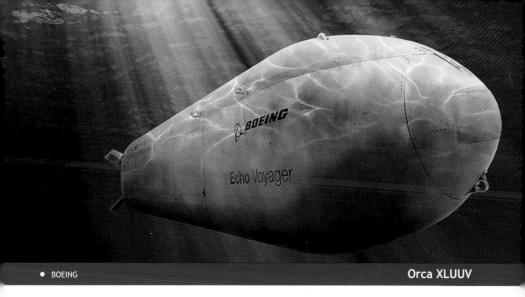

EXTRA LARGE AUTONOMOUS UNDERWATER VEHICLE

In early 2022 the Ministry of Defence launched Project CETUS that is intended to provide the Royal Navy with a large Autonomous Underwater Vehicle costing around £21.5 million. The project will be for a 27 tonnes, 12 metre long demonstrator design which will be known as an XL-AUV. The Government intends to place a contract for the build of the system with the main aim of the project to evaluate how such XL-AUVs could complement the future replacement Astute-class SSN.

The somewhat related Project MANTA is already underway, although that's a 9 metre submarine.

● CROWN COPYRIGHT/MOD

Project MANTA

Royal Fleet Auxiliary

RFA Tideforce and RFA Fort Victoria

Auxiliary vessels are as important and in some cases, more important than the warships they serve. In each auxiliary ship governments and navies have invested time, money and resources into building a system that keeps navies at sea for prolonged periods and to extend the range and reach of a country's military and economic might. Around the globe in the last five years there has been an almost feverish construction boom in naval auxiliaries. The Royal Fleet Auxiliary has not been exempted - with the delivery of the four excellent Tide-class tankers, but as other countries commit to constructing newer, better, faster and larger more capable tonnage, the Ministry of Defence dithers over how best to provide the service with the new ships it needs to deliver dry stores to the fleet.

The MARS programme has been stymied by the usual governmental ineptitude and lack of decision making, while the existing ships are driven on for longer past their shelf life. MARS should have delivered the three planned solid stores ships by now, but in 2021, when a new round of bids were expected to have been sought, nothing has been announced. To be fair the government has been waging a war of sorts against the COVID-19 pandemic and its focus has not been on delivering future capability to the Armed Forces, but a decision must be made soon, after all it takes at least three years to build new ships in the United Kingdom, the Government's stated aim. Less if the Government breaks another promise and has them built overseas against the findings of their own National Shipbuilding Programme.

Today the Royal Fleet Auxiliary is, like the Royal Navy it serves, a shadow of its former scale, complexity and capability. Yet, the ships in this 'fleet within a fleet' often substitute for warships which are needed elsewhere in the world. It is common for a tanker or supply ship to be positioned in the Caribbean during hurricane season or off the West Coast of Africa as a safeguard against the unavailability of the precise and limited number of warships in the Royal Navy.

That being said, the Royal Fleet Auxiliary Service in 2023 (118 years since its formation in 1905), is the backbone that keeps the Royal Navy at sea and supplied with everything from fuel, ammunition, food and 'nutty' (sweets and snacks).

CROWN COPYRIGHT/MOD **RFA Fort Victoria**

SHIPS OF THE ROYAL FLEET AUXILIARY
Pennant Numbers

Ships	P. No.	Page	Ships	P. No.	Page
Tankers			Amphibious Ships		
TIDESPRING	A136	78	LYME BAY	L3007	80
TIDERACE	A137	78	MOUNTS BAY	L3008	80
TIDESURGE	A138	78	CARDIGAN BAY	L3009	80
TIDEFORCE	A139	78			
			Primary Casualty Receiving		
WAVE KNIGHT	A389	77	Ship/Aviation Training Ship		
WAVE RULER	A390	77			
			ARGUS	A135	81
Stores Ship/Tankers					
			Autonomous Mine Warfare		
FORT VICTORIA	A387	79	Support Vessel		
Ocean Surveillance Vessel			MV ISLAND CROWN		84
PROTEUS	---	83			

RFA Mounts Bay

RFA Wave Knight

FAST FLEET TANKERS
WAVE CLASS

Ship	Pennant Number	Completion Date	Builder
WAVE KNIGHT	A389	2002	BAE Systems
WAVE RULER	A390	2002	BAE Systems

Displacement: 31,500 tonnes (FL) **Dimensions:** 196.5m x 28.25m x 10m **Machinery:** Diesel-electric: 4 Wärtsilä DG, 25,514 hp (18.76 MW); 2 GEC Alstom motors with variable speed converters, 19,040 hp (14 MW); 1 shaft; 1 bow and stern thruster **Speed:** 18 knots **Armament:** 2 x Vulcan Phalanx, 2 x 30mm **Aircraft:** Up to 2 Merlin **Complement:** 80 (plus 22 Fleet Air Arm)

Notes: These two ships have a displacement of 31,500 tonnes and are powered by diesel electric propulsion. Each has three replenishment rigs on port and starboard and a Hudson reel type system at the stern. Capacity is 16,900 tonnes of fuel and 915 tonnes of dry stores. The large flight deck and associated hangar can accommodate a pair of Merlin sized helicopters which can be used for vertical replenishment. Both ships have a modern well-equipped medical facility, and their reverse osmosis system can provide 100m3 of fresh water every day. This facility has proven to be of immense value during humanitarian missions such as the annual hurricane season in the Caribbean where fresh water is one of the first essentials for survival.

RFA Tidesurge

FLEET TANKERS
TIDE CLASS

Ship	Pennant Number	Completion Date	Builder
TIDESPRING	A136	2017	Daewoo Shipbuilding
TIDERACE	A137	2018	Daewoo Shipbuilding
TIDESURGE	A138	2018	Daewoo Shipbuilding
TIDEFORCE	A139	2019	Daewoo Shipbuilding

Displacement: 39,000 tonnes (FL) **Dimensions:** 200.9m x 28.6m x 10m **Machinery:** 2 Wärtsilä diesels, 20,394 hp; 2 shafts **Speed:** 26.8 knots **Armament:** 2 x Phalanx CIWS; 2 x 30mm **Aircraft:** 1 x Merlin or Wildcat **Complement:** 63 (plus 26 spare berths)

Notes: At 39,000 tonnes displacement these four ships are the newest and largest ships operated by the Royal Fleet Auxiliary Service. Based on the AEGIR-26 design by BMT Defence Services, they are double-hulled to prevent oil escaping from any possible breaches in compliance with SOLAS (Safety of Life at Sea) regulations for the transportation of oil products around the globe. The ships were designed in parallel with the Queen Elizabeth-class aircraft carriers and their rigs and cranes are compliant with those of the aircraft carriers. Each ship has three abeam RAS(L) stations, one to port and two to starboard for diesel oil, aviation fuel and fresh water. A typical RAS transfer between ships weighs around two tonnes. During a replenishment-at-sea these ships can transfer up to 800 cubic tonnes of fuel an hour. The ships have a large flight deck and hangar for the operation of a single AugustaWestland Wildcat or Merlin helicopter for vertical replenishment operations.

RFA Fort Victoria

REPLENISHMENT SHIPS
FORT CLASS II

Ship	Pennant Number	Completion Date	Builder
FORT VICTORIA	A387	1992	Harland & Wolff

Displacement: 33,675 tonnes Dimensions: 204m x 30m x 9m Machinery: 2 Crossley-Pielstick V-16 diesels, 23,904 hp; 2 shafts Speed: 20 knots Armament: 2 x 30mm Oerlikon / BMARC KAA guns in GAM-B01 mounts, 2 x Phalanx CIWS, 15 cell Sea Wolf Missile System (fitted for but not with) Complement: 95 RFA, 24 MoD Civilians, 15 RN and up to 154 Fleet Air Arm

Notes: In the 1970s the logic of having one replenishment ship for fuel and another for solid supplies was being questioned. Such a profile created waste and an unnecessary line of potential targets for enemy attack to disrupt Royal Navy activities. In response a 'one stop shop' design was formulated that provided fuel, food, supplies, spares, and ammunition in just one hull. The result was a very expensive but extremely capable floating supermarket that can also operate as a mobile base for maritime operations. With a large hangar and flight deck this ship can operate up to 5 Wildcat or 3 Merlin Helicopters. Furthermore, FORT VICTORIA has a 12-bed medical facility that was upgraded in recent years with the latest medical equipment. She is a fleet tanker capable of worldwide operation in support of Royal Navy warships and will eventually be replaced by the first of a new class of Fleet Solid Support Ships around 2028. Confirmation of the intention to acquire the new capability came in July 2022 when Rear-Admiral Paul Marshall, the Senior Responsible Officer for the Fleet Solid Support ship project, told the House of Commons Select Defence Committee that the lead ship of this class was envisaged for service entry in 2028.

LANDING SHIP DOCK (AUXILIARY)
BAY CLASS

Ship	Pennant Number	Completion Date	Builder
LYME BAY	L3007	2007	Swan Hunter
MOUNTS BAY	L3008	2006	BAE Systems
CARDIGAN BAY	L3009	2007	BAE Systems

Displacement: 16,190 tonnes Dimensions: 176.6m x 26.4m x 5.8m Machinery: Diesel-electric; 2 Wärtsilä 8L26 DG, 6,000 hp (4.5 MW); 2 × Wärtsilä 12V26 DG, 9,000 hp (6.7 MW); 2 azimuthing thrusters; 1 bow thruster Speed: 18 knots Armament: 2 x Phalanx CIWS (exact weapons fit varies within the class) Complement: 60

Notes: These three amphibious landing ships can offload embarked troops and armoured vehicles from ship-to-shore using their assigned Landing Craft Vehicle Personnel (LCVP) and Landing Craft Utility (LCU) vessels. These ships are highly versatile and can operate in extremely rough conditions to support amphibious operations and ground forces around the globe.

In 2020 the MoD's intention was to convert one of the Bay-class ships into a Littoral Strike Ship (LSS). Two years later it appears that this plan may have been abandoned as the focus of the LSS conversation has shifted to repurposing the Aviation Training Ship RFA ARGUS to fulfil this emerging role.

Current out of service dates are MOUNTS BAY (2031), CARDIGAN BAY (2031) and LYME BAY (2032).

RFA Argus

PRIMARY CASUALTY RECEIVING SHIP/
AVIATION TRAINING SHIP

Ship	Pennant Number	Completion Date	Builder
ARGUS	A135	1981	Cantieri Navali Breda

Displacement: 28,481 tonnes (Full Load) **Dimensions:** 175.1m x 30.4m x 8.1m
Machinery: 2 Lindholmen Pielstick 18 PC2.5V diesels, 23,400 hp; 2 shafts; 1 bow thruster
Speed: 18 knots **Armament:** 4 x 30mm, 2 x 20mm **Aircraft:** up to 6 Merlin
Complement: 254 (inc 137 FAA)

Notes: ARGUS is the United Kingdom's Primary Casualty Receiving/Aviation Training Ship
in which capacity she operates an extensive Role 3 100 bed medical facility complete
with CT scanner and radiology research and dentistry operating theatre. The care facility
operates with a staff of up to 250 doctors, nurses and support staff. As the ship is armed
(2 x Oerlikon 20mm/85 KAA on GAM-B01 mountings and 4 x 7.62mm GPMGs Mk44
Miniguns) and is not painted in the required white and red crosses, the Geneva
Convention prevents her from being officially classified as a hospital ship.

Her aviation training role is crucial in allowing new naval helicopter pilots at-sea experience
of landing on the pitching and rolling deck at sea in comparative safety. However, the
construction of a casualty evacuation lift, together with a deckhouse aft of the
superstructure, has reduced helicopter capability by one landing spot. Before the
Russian invasion of Ukraine, it was intended that the 42 year-old ARGUS would be
retired from service in 2024 without replacement. In July 2022 it was announced that
the ship would be retained for another-six-years - until 2030 and that she would assume
the future UK Littoral Strike Role after a refit to convert her to this role.

MV Topaz Tangaroa

MV Topaz Tangaroa

OCEAN SURVEILLANCE VESSEL

Ship	Pennant Number	Completion Date	Builder
PROTEUS	TBC	2019	Vard

Displacement: 6,133 tonnes (Full Load) Dimensions: 98.1m x 20.05m x 6m Machinery: Azimuth Propulsion pods Speed: TBC Armament: Fitted for but not necessarily with light weapons Complement: 98 (mix of RFA and RN personnel)

Notes: The former offshore ocean vessel MV TOPAZ TANGAROA was purchased in early 2023 from Topaz Marine for £70 million. She arrived at Cammell Laird shipyard in late January for conversion to meet Ministry of Defence standards which will require the ship to be painted grey and fitted with mounts for military armaments (for but not necessarily with) and military standard communications equipment.

In RFA service she will have the name RFA PROTEUS and will join the RFA in the summer following her short refit. The ship is fitted with a large deck space aft, a heavy lift craft, a helipad and crucially a moonpool in the centre of the ship for the launch and retrieval of underwater reconnaissance and surveillance equipment. She is extremely manoeuvrable with her azimuth propulsion and Global Positioning System allowing her to maintain her position with great accuracy. (Pictured MV Topaz Tangaroa when she was owned by Netherlands-based Van Oord thus flying the Dutch flag).

MV Island Crown

AUTONOMOUS MINE WARFARE SUPPORT VESSEL

Ship	Pennant Number	Completion Date	Builder
MV ISLAND CROWN	TBC	2013	Vard

Displacement: 5,840 tonnes (Full Load) **Dimensions:** 96.8m x 20m x 4.6m **Machinery:** Liquid Natural Gas Propulsion **Speed:** 13.6 knots **Armament:** Fitted for but not necessarily with light weapons **Complement:** up to 100 personnel can be accommodated

Notes: The Ministry of Defence purchased MV ISLAND CROWN for conversion into a mothership for the Royal Navy's growing fleet of autonomous mine warfare boats. Her new name (at time of writing) has yet to be confirmed. The vessel will be based at Faslane and will operate in support of mine countermeasures tasks around UK and European waters.

MV ISLAND CROWN was designed and constructed to serve primarily as an accommodation and 'walk-to-work' vessel for personnel working in the offshore energy industry. The vessel has a workable 561 square metre working deck, a helipad and accommodation spaces for up to 100 personnel.

MT Raleigh Fisher

COMMERCIAL TANKER

Ship	Completion Date	Builder
RALEIGH FISHER	2005	Guangzhou Shipyard, China
CUMBRIAN FISHER	2004	Samho Shipbuilding, Mason, S Korea

Displacement: 22,184 tonnes (GRT); 35,191 tonnes (DWT) **Dimensions:** 172m x 28m x 8.3m **Machinery:** 2SA 5 cylinder Burmeister & Wain diesel, 9,721 hp; 1 shaft; bow thruster **Speed:** 14.5 knots

Notes: In 2019 Maersk took their remaining vessels off the UK Ship Register, exiting the UK Tonnage Tax and ending the training of UK cadets, and sold the tanker MAERSK RALEIGH to UK-based James Fisher & Sons for £9 million. Nick Henry, James Fisher chief executive, said that the renamed tanker - RALEIGH FISHER - would be significant for their tanker business as the vessel is presently contracted to the Ministry of Defence to support the Royal Navy's fuelling needs, both in the UK and abroad, on a five-year contract. The MoD charters the vessel to commercial companies when it is not in use for their own requirements. RALEIGH FISHER is the ex ROSA MAERSK and was renamed and reflagged (to UK flag) in August 2017.

CUMBRIAN FISHER is currently sailing under a Bahamian flag and is occasionally used by the MoD to transfer chemical products. She has a displacement of 8,446 tonnes, with a speed of 10 knots and is much smaller with a length of 127.2m x 20.43m x 6.1m.

Both vessels will be used to move fuel products between the UK, the Falkland Islands and Cyprus, where the MoD supplies RAF Akrotiri with jet fuel. RAF Akrotiri is located on the southern tip of Cyprus and is the service's busiest base.

MV Anvil Point

STRATEGIC SEALIFT RO-RO VESSELS
POINT CLASS

Ship	Pennant Number	Completion Date	Builder
HURST POINT		2002	Flensburger
HARTLAND POINT		2002	Harland & Wolff
EDDYSTONE		2002	Flensburger
ANVIL POINT		2003	Harland & Wolff

Displacement: 10,000 tonnes, 13,300 tonnes (FL) Dimensions: 193m x 26m x 7.6m
Machinery: 2 MaK 94M43 diesels, 21,700 hp; 2 shafts; 2 CP propellors; 1 bow thruster
Speed: 18 knots Complement: 18-22

Notes: Foreland Shipping Limited operated 6 Ro-Ro vessels built at yards in the UK and Germany under a Private Finance Initiative (PFI) deal which was signed with the MoD on 27 June 2002 and runs until 31 December 2024. While the current main focus is on transporting equipment to and from the Middle East/Gulf in support of military activities, the vessels also make regular voyages to the Falkland Islands, Canada and Norway in support of training exercises. Each vessel can carry 130 armoured vehicles and 60 trucks and ammunition or 8,000 tonnes of vehicles. There is 2,650 linear metres of space for vehicles. It can transport up to four helicopters including Chinook, Apache, Merlin and Wildcat. The ships are all named after English lighthouses. They come under the operational umbrella of Defence Supply Chain Operation and Movements (DSCOM), part of the Defence Logistics Organisation. In 2012 the requirement was reduced from six to four ships. BEACHY HEAD and LONGSTONE were subsequently sold.

Serco Marine Services

SD Bountiful (r) & SD Indulgent assisting **HMS Montrose**

Around the coastal waters of the United Kingdom and at several overseas establishments you are likely to see smaller support craft that provide vital facilities to make for the safe and efficient operation of the Royal Navy. These vessels are operated by Serco. Serco have been supporting the Royal Navy since 1996 and provide an end-to-end vessel provisioning service which includes vessel design and acquisition, technical management and operations of a varied fleet of new builds, legacy vessels, conversions and chartered vessels.

Amongst the specialist tasks undertaken by Serco vessels are training support by providing vessels suitable for Royal Navy training, helicopter search and rescue training and the development and deployment of a range of ROVs via the mothership capability delivered by SD NORTHEN RIVER. One of the principal roles of the SERCO fleet is towage in and outside the three naval bases at Devonport, Portsmouth and Faslane plus the transportation of personnel and VIPs from shore bases to warships at sea. In 1996 SERCO inherited a collection of legacy specialist vessels that are increasingly coming to the end of their service lives and the company has an active programme to find innovative solutions to acquire new build or legacy vessels to replace them. Less well-known is the fact that SERCO provides additional services including the transportation of irradiated nuclear fuels for disposal and the provision of 24 hour monitoring and emergency response facilities.

On 16 November 2022 Serco was awarded a contract by the UK Ministry of Defence (MoD) to continue to provide marine services for the Royal Navy. Following the end of the 15-year private finance initiative (PFI) arrangements for the provision of marine services, the new agreement is with the Royal Navy directly. The contract, which is valued at around £200 million, will last for 27 months commencing in December 2022 and follows on directly from the current PFI, ensuring continuity of support. The MoD has an option to extend the contract for up to six months.

SHIPS OF SERCO MARINE SERVICES

Ship	Page	Ship	Page
SD ADEPT	94	SD OMAGH	106
SD ANGELINE	112	SD ORONSAY	106
SD BOUNTIFUL	93	SD PADSTOW	105
SD BOVISAND	103	SD POWERFUL	94
SD CAREFUL	94	SD RAASAY	111
SD CATHERINE	98	SD RELIABLE	93
SD CAWSAND	103	SD RESOURCEFUL	93
SD CHRISTINA	96	SD SOLENT RACER	113
SD CLYDE RACER	113	SD SOLENT SPIRIT	114
SD CLYDE SPIRIT	114	SD SUZANNE	96
SD DEBORAH	96	SD TAMAR RACER	113
SD DEPENDABLE	93	SD TAMAR SPIRIT	114
SD EILEEN	96	SD TEESDALE	108
SD ENGINEER	111	SD TEMPEST	91
SD FAITHFUL	94	SD TILLY	99
SD FLORENCE	97	SD VICTORIA	100
SD FORCEFUL	94	SD WARDEN	101
SD GENEVIEVE	97	SD WATERPRESS	108
SD HELEN	97		
SD HERCULES	95		
SD IMPETUS	90	**Briggs Sub-Contract**	
SD IMPULSE	90		
SD INDEPENDENT	92	CAMERON	115
SD INDULGENT	92	KINGDOM OF FIFE	115
SD INSPECTOR	111		
SD JUPITER	95	SMIT DEE	116
SD KYLE OF LOCHALSH	102	SMIT DART	116
SD MARS	95	SMIT DON	116
SD MOORFOWL	110	SMIT YARE	116
SD MOORHEN	110	SMIT SPEY	116
SD NAVIGATOR	111	SMIT STOUR	117
SD NETLEY	104	SMIT ROTHER	117
SD NEWHAVEN	104	SMIT ROMNEY	117
SD NORTHERN RIVER	109	SMIT CERNE	117
SD NORTON	107	SMIT FROME	117
SD NUTBOURNE	104	SMIT MERRION	117
SD OBAN	106	SMIT PENALLY	117
SD OCEANSPRAY	108	SMIT WEY	117
SD OILMAN	108	SMIT NEYLAND	117

Entries displayed in lighter typeface have been removed from contract and are awaiting sale.

SD Impetus

TUGS

IMPULSE CLASS

Ship	Completion Date	Builder
SD IMPULSE	1993	Richard Dunston (Hull)
SD IMPETUS	1993	Richard Dunston (Hull)

G.R.T.: 319 tonnes **Dimensions:** 32.5m x 10.5m x 5.2m **Machinery:** 2 Allen 8S12 F-BC diesel engines; 3,400 hp; 2 Azimuth thrusters; 1 bow thruster **Speed:** 12 knots **Complement:** 5

Notes: Designed and built specifically to service the Vanguard-class ballistic missile submarines at Faslane with both vessels entering service in 1993, these tugs are used to manoeuvre submarines within the Clyde area and can provide additional services during trials and exercises. IMPULSE was in February 2018 completely modernised for further service. Serco expects a decision on both vessel's future to be made in 2023 or soon thereafter.

SD Tempest

ART 8032 CLASS

Ship	Completion Date	Builder
SD TEMPEST	2017	Damen (Poland)

G.R.T.: 495 tonnes **Dimensions:** 32.9m x 13.2m x 6.2m **Machinery:** 3 Caterpillar 3512C diesels, 5,295 kW; 3 Schottel SRP 1215 CP propellors **Speed:** 13 knots **Complement:** 4

Notes: With a bollard pull of 82 tonnes TEMPEST is the most modern and most powerful tug in the Serco fleet. She was acquired to serve the two Queen Elizabeth-class aircraft carriers at Portsmouth, but when not used in that capacity she provides general harbour towage services. She was ordered in February 2016 and launched in Gdansk (Poland) on 14 September 2016. In February 2017 she arrived at Portsmouth - her homeport.

To facilitate her work with the carriers with their large overhangs TEMPEST is fitted with a foldable mast and is also fitted with a double drum render/recovery aft winch.

SD Independent

ASD 2509 CLASS

Ship	Completion Date	Builder
SD INDEPENDENT	2009	Damen (Netherlands)
SD INDULGENT	2009	Damen (Netherlands)

G.R.T.: 345 tonnes approx **Dimensions:** 25.14m x 9.44m x 4.45m **Machinery:** 2 Caterpillar diesels; 3,500 hp; 2 RR thrusters; 1 bow thruster **Speed:** 13 knots **Complement:** 4

Notes: Both these vessels are homeported at Portsmouth and provide general harbour towage services to warships based there. Each tug has a bollard pull of 40 tonnes and powered by a pair of Azimuth thrusters mounted at the stern. They are frequently seen at Portsmouth cold moving ships around the various stations, a role for which they have been especially fitted out.

SD Bountiful

ATD 2909 CLASS

Ship	Completion Date	Builder
SD RELIABLE	2009	Damen (Netherlands)
SD BOUNTIFUL	2010	Damen (Netherlands)
SD RESOURCEFUL	2010	Damen (Netherlands)
SD DEPENDABLE	2010	Damen (Netherlands)

G.R.T.: 271 tonnes **Dimensions:** 29.14m x 9.98m x 4.41m **Machinery:** 2 Caterpillar diesels; 4,025 hp; 2 RR thrusters **Speed:** 13.1 knots **Complement:** 4 (Portsmouth); 5 (Clyde)

Notes: Built in Poland by the Dutch firm Damen these four Azimuthing Tractor Drive (ATD) tugs are some of the most manoeuvrable tugs in the Serco fleet. Based on a standard Dutch design the four vessels were especially modified for British service with the addition of two double drum towing winches, extensive underwater fendering, fire fighting equipment and space and facilities to carry passengers and a limited number of stores. SD BOUNTIFUL is based at Portsmouth. SD RESOURCEFUL, SD RELIABLE and SD DEPENDABLE are all based on the Clyde.

SD Adept

TWIN UNIT TRACTOR TUGS

Ship	Completion Date	Builder
SD ADEPT	1980	Richard Dunston
SD CAREFUL	1982	Richard Dunston
SD FAITHFUL	1985	Richard Dunston
SD FORCEFUL	1985	Richard Dunston
SD POWERFUL	1985	Richard Dunston

G.R.T.: 384 tonnes **Dimensions:** 38.8m x 9.42m x 4m **Machinery:** 2 Ruston diesels; 2,575 hp; 2 Voith-Schneider propellors **Speed:** 12 knots **Complement:** 5

Notes: These vessels are the survivors of a larger class of naval harbour tugs that have become ubiquitous at Devonport, Portsmouth and on the Clyde since the mid-1980s. Despite their age these venerable tugs are still extremely capable, and some are likely to be refitted to prolong their service lives. All are now based at Devonport.

SD Mars

STAN TUG 2608 CLASS

Ship	Completion Date	Builder
SD HERCULES	2009	Damen (Netherlands)
SD JUPITER	2009	Damen (Netherlands)
SD MARS	2009	Damen (Netherlands)

G.R.T.: 133.92 tonnes **Dimensions:** 26.61m x 8.44m x 4.05m **Machinery:** 2 Caterpillar 3508B TA diesels; 2,200 hp; 2 Van de Giessen Optima nozzles; 90kW HRP hydraulically powered bow thruster **Speed:** 12 knots **Complement:** 4 (6 max)

Notes: The Stan Tug has, since their entry into service in 2009, proved to be a versatile conventional twin-screw tug ideal for coastal and port operations. For naval service, the tug has a comprehensive outfit of equipment enabling them to perform a wide variety of tasks in addition to standard towing operations. Each tug is fitted with two towing winches, a combined anchor windlass and single drum winch located on the foredeck and a double drum towing winch on the after deck. The class features a large and mostly empty deck space aft which has proven to be useful for handling submarine mounted towed array sonars. SD HERCULES is based at Devonport and SD JUPITER is on the Clyde. The third tug, SD MARS is currently being used on the Kyle of Lochalsh performing a variety of functions include towing and passenger transportation.

SD Christina

ASD 2009 CLASS

Ship	Completion Date	Builder
SD CHRISTINA	2010	Damen (Poland)
SD DEBORAH	2010	Damen (Poland)
SD EILEEN	2010	Damen (Poland)
SD SUZANNE	2010	Damen (Poland)

G.R.T.: 120.74 tonnes **Dimensions:** 21.2m x 9.4m x 3.9m **Machinery:** 2 Caterpillar 3508B TA/C diesels; 2,000 hp; 2 Rolls Royce US 155CP thrusters **Speed:** 11 knots **Complement:** 5

Notes: Derived from the hugely successful Damen ASD (Azimuth Stern Drive) 2411 ship handling tug these four vessels have a bollard pull of 30 tonnes. Winches fore and aft, together with a bow thruster, make these tugs suitable for handling smaller surface ships, barge work and assisting with submarine movements, especially in the case of SD DEBORAH and SD EILEEN as the pair are based at Devonport. SD CHRISTINA and SD SUZANNE are based at Portsmouth.

SD Helen

FELICITY CLASS

Ship	Completion Date	Builder
SD FLORENCE	1980	Richard Dunston
SD GENEVIEVE	1980	Richard Dunston
SD HELEN	1974	Richard Dunston

G.R.T.: 88.96 tonnes **Dimensions:** 22.0m x 6.4m x 2.6m **Machinery:** 1 Mirrlees-Blackstone diesel; 615 hp; 1 Voith-Schneider CP propellor **Speed:** 10 knots **Complement:** 4 (Florence - 3)

Notes: Some of the oldest vessels currently in the Serco fleet, these three vessels were delivered between 1974 and 1980 and are used for the movement of small barges around harbours and ports. They have a bollard pull of 5.7 tonnes. SD GENEVIEVE and SD HELEN are based at Portsmouth with SD FLORENCE currently located at Devonport. It is likely that these will be amongst the first vessels replaced by new construction harbour craft.

SD Catherine

PUSHY CAT 1204

Ship	Completion Date	Builder
SD CATHERINE	2008	Damen (Netherlands)

G.R.T.: 29.4 tonnes **Dimensions:** 12.3m x 4.13m x 1.55m **Machinery:** 1 Caterpillar 3056 TA diesel; 165 hp; 1 shaft **Speed:** 8 knots **Complement:** 2

Notes: SD CATHERINE is often seen operating within Portsmouth Harbour and is used as a general line runner and harbour workboat. She is powered by a single Caterpillar 3056 TA diesel driving a single screw. Additionally, she is fitted with a propulsion nozzle and twin rudders giving her a 2.1 tonnes bollard pull.

SD Tilly

STAN TUG 1405

Ship	Completion Date	Builder
SD TILLY	2009	Damen (Netherlands)

G.R.T.: 45 tonnes **Dimensions:** 14.55m x 4.98m x 1.8m **Machinery:** 2 Caterpillar diesels; 600 hp; 2 Van de Giessen nozzles **Speed:** 9 knots **Complement:** 3

Notes: Based at Devonport, SD TILLY is a general purpose inshore and harbour tug and is mostly used as a general workboat and line handler. Her design is an upgraded twin screwed version of the Pushy Cat 1204 with a larger and more powerful bow thruster giving her an 8 tonnes bollard pull capability.

SD Victoria

WORLDWIDE SUPPORT VESSEL

Ship	Completion Date	Builder
SD VICTORIA	2010	Damen (Romania)

G.R.T.: 3,522 tonnes **Dimensions:** 83m x 16m x 4.5m **Machinery:** 2 Caterpillar 3516B diesels; 4,000 hp; 2 shafts; CP propellors; 1 bow thruster **Speed:** 14 knots **Complement:** 16 (accommodation for 72)

Notes: SD VICTORIA was built in Romania at Damen's Galatz shipyard and at 83 metres in length is the second largest vessel in the Serco Marine Services fleet. She has twin controllable pitch propellors driven by a pair of Caterpillar 3516B diesel engines. She is based at Greenock's Great Harbour and was designed to provide a full range of services to support training missions anywhere around the globe. Although Serco Marine Services have her available for commercial charter she is mostly used in support of British military training and exercises. Inside the ship are large well-equipped spaces, set up as classrooms, briefing rooms and an operations room. Elsewhere onboard spaces have been allocated to workshop facilities. Her most notable feature is the large crane on the stern. There is provision to carry and operate a variety of small craft such as Rigid Inflatable Boats (RIBs), and forward of the bridge there is a helicopter winching deck.

SD Warden

TRIALS VESSEL

Ship	Completion Date	Builder
SD WARDEN	1989	Richards

Displacement: 626 tonnes **Dimensions:** 49m x 11m x 4m **Machinery:** 2 Ruston diesels; 4,000 hp; 2 shafts; CP propellors **Speed:** 15 knots **Complement:** 11

Notes: Serco Marine Services, as part of their contract with the Ministry of Defence, provide ships and facilities for trials of future equipment for the Royal Navy. In support of these activities Serco operates SD WARDEN out of the Kyle of Lochalsh. Her principal role, however, is to act as a Mooring and Weapons Recovery vessel at the British Underwater Test and Evaluation Centre (BUTEC) where her work supports the testing of future underwater weapon systems, sonar technologies and the evaluation of ships' radiated noise profiles in the water. In recent years SD WARDEN has been a focal point for the work undertaken by QinetiQ in the development of Remotely Operated Vehicles (ROVs). Serco advises that the decommissioning plans for SD WARDEN will be delayed until 2023 or beyond.

SD Kyle of Lochalsh

TRIALS VESSEL

Ship	Completion Date	Builder
SD KYLE OF LOCHALSH	1997	Abels Boatbuilders

Displacement: 120 tonnes Dimensions: 24.35m x 9m x 3.45m Machinery: 2 Caterpillar diesels; 2,992 hp; 2 shafts Speed: 10.5 knots Complement: 4

Notes: Built in 1997 by Abels Boatbuilders in Bristol as the twin-screw tug MCS LENIE, SD KYLE OF LOCHALSH has spent most of her career in the service of Serco Marine Services in Scottish waters. In 2008, after some years on contract, she was purchased from Maritime Craft Services (Clyde) Ltd and renamed. She has since been used in trials and operations at Kyle of Lochalsh. She has a bollard pull 26 tonnes.

SD Cawsand

TENDERS
STORM CLASS

Ship	Completion Date	Builder
SD BOVISAND	1997	FBM (Cowes)
SD CAWSAND	1997	FBM (Cowes)

G.R.T.: 225 tonnes **Dimensions:** 23m x 11m x 2m **Machinery:** 2 Caterpillar diesels; 1,224 hp; 2 shafts **Speed:** 15 knots **Complement:** 5

Notes: These tenders have a distinctive appearance and are amongst the most frequently seen vessels darting around Plymouth harbour and up the River Tamar. They were bought at a cost of £6.5 million apiece and have a SWATH hull form (Small Waterplane Area Twin Hull) which offered improved performance. They are used to support the work of Flag Officer Sea Training (FOST) and with their relatively high speed can transfer staff quickly and comfortably to and from warships and auxiliaries within and beyond the confines of Plymouth breakwater.

SD Netley

NEWHAVEN CLASS

Ship	Completion Date	Builder
SD NEWHAVEN	2000	Aluminium SB
SD NUTBOURNE	2000	Aluminium SB
SD NETLEY	2001	Aluminium SB

Displacement: 77 tonnes (45 grt) Dimensions: 18.3m x 6.8m x 1.88m Machinery: 2 Cummins diesels; 710 hp; 2 shafts Speed: 10 knots Complement: 2/3 Crew (60 passengers)

Notes: Like the Storm Class, the Newhaven Class uses the same SWATH hull form and are generally utilised in the general passenger duties role within harbours and ports. SD NETLEY and SD NUTBOURNE are based at Portsmouth, while SD NEWHAVEN is currently located at Devonport where she operates in support of Flag Officer Sea Training (FOST). SD NEWHAVEN differs slightly from her two sisters as she has been modified with strengthened forward bollard and with the addition of transfer wings to enable underway personnel transfers.

PADSTOW CLASS

Ship	Completion Date	Builder
SD PADSTOW	2000	Aluminium SB

Displacement: 77 tonnes (45 grt) Dimensions: 18.3m x 6.8m x 1.88m Machinery: 2 Cummins diesels; 710 hp; 2 shafts Speed: 10 knots Complement: 2/3 Crew (60 passengers)

Notes: SD PADSTOW is another MCA IV, VI and VIA Passenger Vessel based at Devonport. Built in Hampshire by Aluminium Shipbuilders she has been modified along similar lines to SD NEWHAVEN in order to facilitate the speedy and safe transfer of personnel to other vessels whilst underway.

SD Oban

OBAN CLASS

Ship	Completion Date	Builder
SD OBAN	2000	McTay Marine
SD ORONSAY	2000	McTay Marine
SD OMAGH	2000	McTay Marine

G.R.T.: 199 tonnes Dimensions: 27.7m x 7.30m x 3.75m Machinery: 2 Cummins diesels; 1,050 hp; 2 Kort-nozzles Speed: 10 knots Complement: 4 Crew (60 passengers)

Notes: Built to replace elderly tenders used since the 1970s, in 2000 this trio of vessels are MCA Class IIA Passenger Vessels. SD OBAN is primarily assigned the duties associated with Flag Officer Sea Training (FOST) and as such operates principally out of Devonport. SD ORANSAY and SD OMAGH are currently based on the Clyde and used mostly for general passenger duties but have a secondary role in the Cargo Ship VIII(A) role.

SD Norton

PERSONNEL FERRY

Ship	Completion Date	Builder
SD NORTON	1989	FBM Marine

G.R.T.: 21 tonnes **Dimensions:** 15.8m x 5.5m x 1.5m **Machinery:** 2 Mermaid Turbo diesels; 280 hp; 2 shafts **Speed:** 13 knots **Complement:** 2

Notes: Conceived as the first of a projected series of vessels to replace the once numerous fleet tenders SD NORTON was a prototype vessel designed to carry 30 passengers or 2 tonnes of stores and has a relatively simple catamaran hull form. The projected extra vessels never materialised.

SD Teesdale

COASTAL OILER

Ship	Completion Date	Builder
SD TEESDALE	1976	Yorkshire Drydock Co.

G.R.T.: 499 tonnes **Dimensions:** 43.86m x 9.5m x 3.92m **Speed:** 8 knots **Complement:** 5

Notes: SD TEESDALE is an oil products tanker that was taken up from commercial use by the company of John H Whitaker. In commercial service the ship was known as TEESDALE H. In Serco Marine service she is listed as a parcel tanker capable of delivering diesel and aviation fuel products together with delivering/receiving compensating water. She is self-propelled by two Aquamaster thrusters.

A Diesel Lighter Barge, SD OILMAN, and a Water Lighter Barge, SD WATERPRESS, are operated on the Clyde. A further barge, SD OCEANSPRAY, a Liquid Mixed Lighter Barge, is based at Portsmouth.

SD OILMAN has a displacement of 222 tonnes and is a Damen DBa 3009 lighter. She was built in Poland and completed by Damen in the Netherlands in 2009. She has a length of 30.4m, with a width of 8.5m and serves as a non-propelled barge. SD OCEANSPRAY is a 764 tonnes non-propelled barge with a length of 43.22m and a width of 15.4m. She was constructed by Crist in Gdansk, Poland and completed in 2010.

SD Northern River

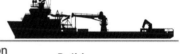

MULTI-PURPOSE VESSEL

Ship	Completion Date	Builder
SD NORTHERN RIVER	1998	Myklebust (Norway)

G.R.T.: 3,605 tonnes **Dimensions:** 92.8m x 18.8m x 4.9m **Machinery:** 2 Bergen diesels; 9,598 hp; 2 shafts; CP propellors; 2 bow thrusters **Speed:** 14 knots **Complement:** 14

Notes: SD NORTHERN RIVER is the largest vessel operated by Serco Marine Services and is listed as a multi-purpose auxiliary ship. In March 2012 she was bought from Deep Ocean AS and entered service with Serco to perform a wide range of support taskings including towing, boarding training and submarine escort. Built as an offshore support vessel she boasts a large open and flat work deck which can be quickly and easily modified to suit the tasks required through the installation of modulated palleted containers including specialist sonar equipment. NORTHERN RIVER can also conduct nuclear emergency and submarine rescue support missions. The latter requires the embarkation, fitting and operation of specialist ROVs, escape vessels and Transfer Under Pressure (TUP) facilities on the after deck, together with the embarkation of an additional 40 personnel.

SD Moorhenl

DIVING SUPPORT VESSELS
MOOR CLASS

Ship	Completion Date	Builder
SD MOORFOWL	1989	McTay Marine
SD MOORHEN	1989	McTay Marine

Displacement: 518 tonnes **Dimensions:** 36m x 12m x 2m **Machinery:** 2 Cummins diesels; 796 hp; 2 Aquamasters; 1 bow thruster **Speed:** 8 knots **Complement:** 10

Notes: Designed as a powered mooring lighter for use within sheltered coastal waters, the lifting horns have been removed from the bows of both vessels when they were converted to Diving Support Vessels. They are used by the Defence Diving School for diving training in the Kyle of Lochalsh. Serco advises that the decommissioning plans for the Moor Class will be delayed.

SD Navigator

MULTICAT 2510 CLASS

Ship	Completion Date	Builder
SD NAVIGATOR	2009	Damen (Netherlands)
SD RAASAY	2010	Damen (Netherlands)

Displacement: 362 tonnes   Dimensions: 25.54m x 10.64m x 2.34m   Machinery: 2 Caterpillar diesels; 957 hp; 2 shafts   Speed: 8.4 knots   Complement: 3 (plus up to 12 additional personnel)

Notes: SD NAVIGATOR is equipped for buoy handling with a single 9 tonnes capacity crane. She is capable of supporting diving operations. SD NAVIGATOR is managed from Devonport but operates between Devonport and Portsmouth. SD RAASAY is based at the Kyle of Lochalsh and is fitted with two cranes for torpedo recovery and support diving training. Two similar, but smaller vessels, SD INSPECTOR (ex-DMS EAGLE until March 2003 and ex-FORTH INSPECTOR until December 2007) and SD ENGINEER, operate from Portsmouth and Devonport respectively. SD INSPECTOR is a Utility Vessel that was built in 2001 with a length overall of 18.7m and a width of 8m. SD ENGINEER is a Work Vessel that was built in 1996 with a length overall of 17.49m and a width of 8.06m.

SD Angeline

MULTICAT 2613 CLASS

Ship	Completion Date	Builder
SD ANGELINE	2015	Damen (Netherlands)

Displacement: 657 tonnes **Dimensions:** 25.5m x 13.6m x 4m **Machinery:** 2 Caterpillar C32 TTA diesels; 2 Promarin fixed pitch propellors; bow thruster **Speed:** 10.1 knots **Complement:** Accommodation for 8 persons, consisting of four double crew cabins

Notes: SD ANGELINE was ordered in April 2014 and was accepted by the MoD in April 2015. Built at the request of the MoD to provide support in Faslane Naval Base primarily to submarines, but can undertake other naval base work. Her total power output is 2,850 kW with a bollard pull of 30.8 tonnes. The installed crane has a capacity of 15 tonnes.

SD Solent Racer

STAN TENDER 1505 CLASS

Ship	Completion Date	Builder
SD CLYDE RACER	2008	Damen (Netherlands)
SD SOLENT RACER	2008	Damen (Netherlands)
SD TAMAR RACER	2008	Damen (Netherlands)

G.R.T.: 25.19 tonnes **Dimensions:** 15.2m x 4.8m x 1.25m **Machinery:** 2 Caterpillar diesels; 1,100 hp; 2 shafts **Speed:** 26 knots **Complement:** 2 (+ 8 Passengers)

Notes: Frequently seen operating within Royal Navy dockyards and approaches, these fast twin-screw workboats are built from strong aluminium. They regularly transfer pilots, VIPs and passengers to and from warships and can also undertake port security operations. Each boat's name gives an indication to which port they are assigned.

SD Solent Spirit

STAN TENDER 1905 CLASS

Ship	Completion Date	Builder
SD CLYDE SPIRIT	2008	Damen (Netherlands)
SD SOLENT SPIRIT	2008	Damen (Netherlands)
SD TAMAR SPIRIT	2008	Damen (Netherlands)

G.R.T.: 43.3 tonnes   Dimensions: 19.2m x 5.3m x 1.8m   Machinery: 2 Caterpillar diesels; 2,200 hp; 2 shafts   Speed: 25 knots   Complement: 2 (+ 10 passengers)

Notes: Steel hull with aluminium superstructure. Special propellor tunnels are fitted to increase propulsion efficiency and to reduce vibration and noise levels. These vessels are able to operate safely and keep good performance in wind speeds up to Force 6 and wave heights of 2 metres. Employed on transfer on pilots, VIPs and personnel. Each boat's name gives an indication to which port they are assigned.

Kingdom of Fife

ANCHOR HANDLING TUG

Ship	Completion Date	Builder
KINGDOM OF FIFE	2008	Damen (Romania)

Displacement: 1,459 tonnes **Dimensions:** 61.2m x 13.5m x 4.75m **Machinery:** 2 Caterpillar diesels, 2,720 hp each; 1 shaft; bow thruster **Speed:** 13.7 knots **Complement:** 18

Notes: KINGDOM OF FIFE is operated by Briggs Marine under a 15-year £100million contract from Serco to support navigation buoy maintenance and mooring support for the Royal Navy. This requires the company to regularly inspect, service and repair where necessary, over 350 moorings, navigation buoys and targets around the UK's coastline and those in the Falkland Islands, Gibraltar and Cyprus. A second vessel operated by Briggs Marine is the former Serco vessel CAMERON which can, when required, be fitted with a decompression chamber for teams of deep sea divers servicing the buoys and navigational aids.

Cameron

Smit Dee

AIRCREW TRAINING VESSELS

Ship	Comp Date	Builder	Base Port
SMIT DEE	2003	BES Rosyth	Buckie
SMIT DART	2003	BES Rosyth	Plymouth
SMIT DON	2003	BES Rosyth	Blyth
SMIT YARE	2003	FBMA Cebu	Great Yarmouth
SMIT SPEY	2003	FBMA Cebu	Plymouth

G.R.T.: 95.86 GRT **Dimensions:** 27.6m x 6.6m x 1.5m **Machinery:** 2 Cummins diesels; 1,400 hp; 2 shafts; 1 centreline waterjet; 305hp **Speed:** 20 knots **Complement:** 6

Notes: The service for Marine Support to Range Safety and Aircrew Training is provided by SMIT International (Scotland) Ltd. A new seven year contract for £39m started in April 2018 and will run for five years until March 2023, with an option to extend for a further two years. These vessels provide support to aircrew training such as sea survival drills, various helicopter exercises, target towing and other general marine support tasks. They also participate in Navy Command sea training serials, particularly boarding exercises and force protection exercises involving fast attack craft scenarios. SMIT DART completed as a passenger vessel with a larger superstructure.

Smit Rother

RANGE SAFETY VESSELS

Ship	Comp Date	Builder
SMIT STOUR	2003	Maritime Partners Norway
SMIT ROTHER	2003	Maritime Partners Norway
SMIT ROMNEY	2003	Maritime Partners Norway
SMIT CERNE	2003	Maritime Partners Norway
SMIT FROME	2003	Maritime Partners Norway
SMIT MERRION	2003	Maritime Partners Norway
SMIT PENALLY	2003	Maritime Partners Norway
SMIT WEY	2003	Maritime Partners Norway
SMIT NEYLAND	2003	Maritime Partners Norway

G.R.T.: 7.0 GRT **Dimensions:** 12.3m x 2.83m x 0.89m **Machinery:** 2 Volvo Penta diesels; 680 hp; 2 Hamilton waterjets **Speed:** 28 knots **Complement:** 2

Notes: A class of 12m Fast Patrol Craft which provide a range safety service to 7 land based ranges across the UK. They also participate in Navy Command Sea Training serials including participation in Fast Attack Craft scenarios. Part of a £39 million contract the MoD awarded to SMIT International (Scotland) Ltd in April 2018.

AWB Storm

ARMY VESSELS
WORK BOATS

Vessel	Pennant Number	Completion Date	Builder
STORM	WB41	2008	Warbreck Eng.
DIABLO	WB42	2008	Warbreck Eng.
MISTRAL	WB43	2008	Warbreck Eng.
SIROCCO	WB44	2008	Warbreck Eng.

Displacement: 48 tonnes Dimensions: 14.75m x 4.30m Machinery: 2 John Deere Diesels; 402 hp; 2 shafts Speed: 10 knots Complement: 4

Notes: These work boats are part of the Army's strategic port operations in Southampton, but can be transported by a 'mother ship' to other ports and places like Iraq. Are often used as tugs for Mexeflotes, positioning other pontoon equipment and for handling flexible pipelines. They have a firefighting capability. The Army also operate a number of smaller Combat Support Boats. Built by RTK Marine/VT Halmatic (now BAE) these are fast and rugged small craft, 8.8m long with a twin Hamilton waterjet propulsion system powered by twin 210 hp diesel engines.

HMC Speedwell

I n the last decade, Border Force has been tasked with the unsavoury task of trying to stem the tide of illegal immigration across the English Channel. Often Border Force vessels appear in the media with their decks full of immigrants who have been rescued from the world's busiest seaway from their ill-equipped inflatable boats. By November 2022, 40,000 people had attempted the hazardous crossing, well in excess of the figure for 2021.

Border Force is a law enforcement command within the Home Office. Their official role is to secure the UK border by conducting immigration and customs controls for people and goods entering the UK. This rather generalised description of their role does not do the Border Force the justice it deserves. Additionally, Border Force is responsible for the collection of intelligence and for alerting the police and security services of suspicious activities, and for the searching of baggage, vehicles and cargo for illicit goods and illegal immigrants. In this role Border Force facilitates the legitimate movement of individuals and trade to and from the United Kingdom.

Border Force's responsibilities are not confined to the maritime environment as they are also responsible for airports, postal depots and railways, including Eurostar and Eurotunnel services at Folkestone. Border Force is split into five operational regions (Central, Heathrow, North, South and South-East and Europe).

BORDER FORCE PATROL VESSELS

HMC Valiant

BORDER FORCE
STAN PATROL 4207 CLASS

Vessel	Callsign	Completion Date	Builder
SEARCHER	ZQNK9	2002	Damen
SEEKER	ZQNL2	2001	Damen
VALIANT	MBLL8	2004	Damen
VIGILANT	ZITI4	2003	Damen

G.R.T.: 238 tonnes **Dimensions:** 42.8m x 7.11m x 2.52m **Machinery:** 2 Caterpillar 3516B diesels, 2 shafts; 2 4-blade controllable pitch propellors; 1 Promac bow thruster **Speed:** 26+ knots **Complement:** 12

Notes: These vessels are able to remain at sea for extended periods and in heavy weather conditions. They are mostly deployed on a risk-led or intelligence-led basis detecting prohibited and restricted goods, boarding and searching ships and providing a law enforcement presence in remote and inaccessible areas. Vessels are prefixed HMC for Her Majesty's Cutter. They were built at the Damen Shipyard in the Netherlands and all have a steel hull with an aluminium superstructure.All are based at Portsmouth and are normally not armed with fixed firearms, nor are crew armed. What is often taken to be a gun on the bow of the cutters is in fact a water hose. A 7m rigid inflatable boat (RIB) can be launched from the stern slipway.

TELKKÄ CLASS

Vessel	Callsign	Completion Date	Builder
PROTECTOR	2GWY9	2002	UKI Workboat

Displacement: 434 tonnes Dimensions: 49.7m x 7.3m x 3.65m Machinery: 2 Wärtsilä 12V200 diesels, 7,240 hp; 2 shafts; CP propellor; bow and stern thrusters Speed: 22 knots Complement: 12

Notes: HMC PROTECTOR (not to be confused with HMS PROTECTOR) was acquired in August 2013 and commissioned in March 2014. She is the former Finnish Border Agency vessel TAVI. She replaced HMC SENTINEL which was retired in 2013. All HMC cutters operate 24 hours a day, 365 days per year, through the employment of dual crews. There are ten crews for the five Border Force cutters comprising 120 seagoing staff, working two weeks on and two weeks off.

Border Force also operate 10 Jet Ski's (known as Personal Water-Craft) equipped with rubberised fenders to prevent damaging their fibreglass skins when coming alongside vessels during boarding operations and 3 Rigid Inflatable Boats for a variety of tasks in sheltered inland waters around the coastline.

HMC Hurricane

WINDFARM SUPPORT VESSELS

Vessel	Callsign	Completion Date	Builder
DEFENDER	---	2013	South Boats
RANGER	---	2014	South Boats
TYPHOON	---	2016	Aluminium Marine
HURRICANE	---	2016	Aluminium Marine

Displacement: 59 tonnes **Dimensions:** 23m x 9m x 1.4m **Machinery:** 2 x MTU 10V2000M72 and 2x Rolls Royce 56A3 **Speed:** 27 knots **Complement:** 3

Notes: Until recently, the UK Border Force relied for Channel patrols mainly upon a fleet drawn from its inventory of five offshore patrol vessels backed up by six converted oil rig rescue craft deployed as coastal patrol craft. However, the fleet has been discreetly upgraded by the phased introduction of a flotilla of four chartered early-model catamaran craft that were formerly operated as windfarm support vessels (WFSVs). WFSVs were selected as they offer stability and increased carrying capacity. The introduction of these craft is the latest attempt to meet the challenge posed by mass irregular migration. Since April 2022, English Channel security patrols by the UKBF have been carried out under the overall direction of the Royal Navy. Under an arrangement scheduled to run until early 2023, the navy provides a search radar-equipped River-class OPV as a command ship along with four coastal patrol craft as well as intelligence support and aerial surveillance.

HMC Nimrod

DELTA ARRC 190 CLASS

Vessel	Callsign	Completion Date	Builder
EAGLE	ZCPH5	2006	Holyhead Marine/Delta ARCC
NIMROD	2JQP9	2006	Holyhead Marine/Delta ARCC
ALERT	2JQQ2	2006	Holyhead Marine/Delta ARCC
ACTIVE	2JQQ3	2006	Holyhead Marine/Delta ARCC
HUNTER	ZCOO3	2006	Holyhead Marine/Delta ARCC
SPEEDWELL		2006	Holyhead Marine/Delta ARCC
ASTUTE		2006	Holyhead Marine/Delta ARCC
ARDENT		2006	Holyhead Marine/Delta ARCC

Displacement: 29 GRT Dimensions: 17.75m x 5.63m x 0.9m Machinery: 2 Caterpillar C18 diesels, 1,727 hp; 2 Hamilton waterjets Speed: 34 knots Complement: 6

Notes: Starting in 2016, to boost the number of vessels patrolling the UK coastline, eight ex-BP Project Jigsaw rescue craft, built by Holyhead Marine (Holyhead) and Delta ARCC (Stockport), were acquired by Border Force. They are termed Coastal Patrol Vessels within Border Force. As well as carrying out regular patrols of UK waters, CPVs will act on intelligence provided by law enforcement and international partners. Callsigns are displayed on the superstructure roof forward of the bridge. The design includes a deep-vee fibre-reinforced plastic hull design and can return to the upright position if capsized.

I n concert with virtually all the world's leading naval powers, the Royal Navy has had to reflect on the naval air wing of the future. What capabilities will be available and what sort of mix of manned and unmanned vehicles will comprise the air wing? Indeed, is there a role for manned aircraft in what has been named as Future Maritime Aviation Force (FMAF)?

Drones and unmanned aerial vehicles (UAVs) and a wide variety of other acronyms will dominate the vision for the Royal Navy and with a projected in-service timeline of 2030 the future is nearer than you think. The principal aim of FAMF is to increase the available mass, range, persistence and resilience of the Royal Navy airwing flying from the two Queen Elizabeth-class aircraft carriers, and with the use of small and medium sized Uncrewed Aerial Systems (UASs) virtually every ship, whatever it's displacement, could have some form of aerial component to its arsenal and available equipment by the end of this decade.

The introduction of new autonomous and digitally linked air vehicles will eventually possibly lead to the phasing out or supplementation of other older, more expensive and less reliable conventional and traditional systems and aircraft. New pilots entering the Royal Navy should not fear however, as the projected out-of-service timeframe for F-35B Lightning II aircraft is in the order of the 2050-60s. FAMF is primarily a Royal Navy project, but with the merging of F-35B Lightning II aircraft from the RN and RAF aboard aircraft carriers it is increasingly becoming a joint venture. Each service has technical insight, experience and ideas that will benefit the other mutually in their individual programmes.

One of the key words mentioned is mass. With fewer than 70 F-35B Lightning II strike aircraft available between the RN and RAF, there is clearly insufficient to satisfy all needs and to quickly replace battle damaged or lost aircraft in time of conflict. To create mass, there needs to be loads of aircraft – QED UAVs. Relatively simple, relatively cheap and easily mass produced, UAVs can act in 'swarms' given the right computer codes and instructions. The enemy defences could be swamped with targets allowing just enough to get through and attack, and all without risking the lives of aircrew. More sophisticated UAS are being developed that can act as tanker aircraft for manned and unmanned aerial vehicles whilst others are being developed with an ever increasingly complex suite of electronic sensors which can be placed in harms way but without the risks associated with manned aircraft. Such larger UAS may require specialist handling equipment on ships capable of operating them such as catapults and arrestor gear.

In the medium to long term, there is, however, no alternative than manned platforms in the skies over the oceans. The Human Eyeball No 1 is still one of the most advanced and sensitive sensors ever and will be hard to replicate. The centrepiece of Royal Navy maritime aviation will, for the next thirty-forty years, be the Lockheed Martin F-35B Lightning II Joint Strike Fighter. By 2027 the first 48 aircraft will have been delivered. The remainder of what is projected to be less than 80 in total will arrive in small numbers over the coming decades. It is unlikely that by 2030 the total available F-35Bs in the United Kingdom will be around 55 airframes. These aircraft will have been upgraded to take the latest weaponry including the SPEAR-3 standoff weapon and the Meteor BVRAAM. They will also have had Block 4 software upgrades installed. In 2023 the F-35B lacks a potent anti-ship/land attack missile but political deals are being made behind the scenes that could see the aircraft equipped with a suitable weapon as part of the FCASW programme, although the weapon systems will probably not materialise until around 2030. 809 NAS squadron, the second RN frontline F-35B Squadron was supposed to be operational this year, but a shortage of aircraft delivered to the UK has meant this has been delayed to 2026. Four years after that a third, this time, Royal Air Force Squadron, will be stood up.

While officials at Farnborough International Airshow in July 2022 spoke of new partnerships in the development of joint European naval helicopter programmes to replace legacy airframes, the timeline for development will see new aircraft entering service in the mid-2030s. The RN Merlin fleet's lifetime will be pushed out to until 2040 before replacements are purchased. This is a major ask because the Mk2s were expected to be retired in 2029 and the Mk4s (most recently refurbished) in 2030. The British defence budget has no available funding for replacement aircraft so the hope is continual upgrades of avionics and mission systems will suffice. 2023 will also likely see a decision made on replacing the Merlin engines.

Wildcat has proven to be an agile, capable and lethal maritime helicopter and by 2030 it will have even more teeth with the installation of the Sea Venom missile in addition to the already operational Martlet missile. Not visible to the casual observer is the development of a new Tactical Data Link (TDL) for the Wildcat that will make the aircraft a much more effective anti-submarine warfare asset. Wildcats do, however, still lack a dipping sonar, a decision on the purchase of these is yet to be taken. By 2030 the Wildcat, it is hoped, will also mount the Future Lightweight Torpedo as a direct replacement for the Sting Ray which has been in service since the early 1980s.

Perhaps the most exciting and challenging current project will see the Royal Air Force and Royal Navy, and to a lesser extent the British Army, partner on Project VIXEN. For the Royal Navy this project could led to the reconfiguring of the flight decks of the two Queen Elizabeth-class aircraft carriers to include catapults and arresting gear for unmanned aerial vehicles. These so called 'loyal wingman' UAS will act as force multipliers for the F-35B Lightnings and could even potentially attack in swarms. The RAF's version of Project VIXEN is named Mosquito and the first example is scheduled to fly in 2023. These drones, if operated from the RN's carriers, could also perform the air-to-air refuelling (AAR) role in a similar fashion to the US Navy's MQ-25 Stingrays.

In March 2022 the BAE Hawk T1 aircraft were withdrawn from service. These aircraft were used in an aggressor role for live defence training for RN crews in defence against aerial attacks. The effects of their withdrawal has been minimised by the provision of Hawk T2 jets of the Royal Air Force. However, the solution is not ideal as these jets have to fly from bases hundreds of miles away and have limited time on station as a result. Project VAMPIRE, however, could provide a partial solution by providing drones to simulate fast jet attacks. In January 2022 the Government issued an invitation to industry to tender for 4 air vehicles, a launcher and a control station, with options for another 10 aircraft and 2 launchers in the future. At the same time another tender for a large medium lift tethered UAV to be attached to a moving ship was issued. The UAV, the tender stated, must have a lift capability of between 1-25kg and to remain airborne for at least 24 hours. This concept would give any warship an additional early warning sensor as from the height of the aircraft it can see further than any mast-based sensor.

The biggest challenge of all for the Royal Navy's Future Maritime Aviation Force is how to achieve these lofty aims within the space of seven years. 2030 is closer than one thinks, and any hiccups or financial problems could easily upset the timescale. The challenge, however, is not solely on the shoulders of the military, it is being shared by industry and business partners who have a vested interest to make these systems and concepts succeed.

CROWN COPYRIGHT/MOD

AIRCRAFT & UNITS

NAVY COMMAND SQUADRONS

809 NAS	Merlin HM2	TAG/RNAS Culdrose
814 NAS	Merlin HM2	TAG/RNAS Culdrose
815 NAS	Wildcat HMA2	Flights/RNAS Yeovilton
820 NAS	Merlin HM2	TAG/RNAS Culdrose
824 NAS	Merlin HM2	Training/RNAS Culdrose
825 NAS	Wildcat HMA2	Training/RNAS Yeovilton
849 NAS	Merlin HM2 'Crowsnest'	TAG/RNAS Culdrose
700X NAS		RNAS Culdrose
727 NAS	Tutor T1	Grading/RNAS Yeovilton
FOST Flight	Dauphin 2	HMNB Devonport

JOINT FORCE LIGHTNING

17 Sqn	F-35B Lightning II	Edwards AFB - USA
617 Sqn	F-35B Lightning II	TAG/RAF Marham
207 Sqn	F-35B Lightning II (projected)	Training/RAF Marham

JOINT HELICOPTER COMMAND

845 NAS	Merlin HC4/3i	TAG/RNAS Yeovilton
846 NAS	Merlin HC4/3i	TAG/RNAS Yeovilton
847 NAS	Wildcat AH1	TAG/RNAS Yeovilton
7 Sqn	Chinook HC4/4A/5	TAG/RAF Odiham
18 Sqn	Chinook HC4/4A/5	TAG/RAF Odiham
27 Sqn	Chinook HC4/4A/5	TAG/RAF Odiham
28(AC) Sqn	Chinook HC4/4A/5	Training/RAF Odiham
1 Regt.	Wildcat AH1	TAG/RNAS Yeovilton
3 Regt.	Apache AH1	TAG/AAC Wattisham
4 Regt.	Apache AH1	TAG/AAC Wattisham

MILITARY FLYING TRAINING SYSTEM

72(R) Sqn	Tucano T1	1 FTS/RAF Linton-on-Ouse
703 Sqn	Tutor T1	3 FTS/RAF Barkston Heath
750 NAS	Avenger T1	RNAS Culdrose
705 Sqn	Juno HT1	DHFS/RAF Shawbury

Training for pilots on the Hawk T1 have been halted due to engine problems. Therefore all references to Hawk T1 have been taken out.

Leonardo Helicopters MERLIN HM2

Role: Anti-submarine search and strike; maritime surveillance
Engines: 3 x Rolls Royce/Turbomeca RTM 322 each developing 2,100 shp
Length: 74' 10" **Rotor:** diameter 61' **Height:** 21' 10"
Max. Weight: 32,120lb **Max. Speed:** 167 knots **Crew:** 1/2 pilots, 1 observer, 1 aircrewman
Avionics: Blue Kestrel radar; Orange Reaper ESM; Folding Light Acoustic System for helicopters (FLASH); AQS-903 acoustic processor; Wescam MX-15 electro-optical/IR camera; defensive aids including Directional Infrared Countermeasures (DIRCM), AN/AAR-57 radar warning system, chaff and flare dispensers;
Armament: Up to 4 Stingray torpedoes or Mark 11 depth charges; 1 x M3M 0.5" machine-gun in cabin door and 1 x 7.62mm machine-gun in cabin window

Squadron Service: 814, 820, 824, 849 Naval Air Squadrons

Notes: 814 NAS is the biggest Merlin Mk2 helicopter Squadron that the Royal Navy ever had (it merged with the decommissioned 829 Naval Air Squadron at the end of March 2018). The merger might signal the start of the execution of the MoD forward plan which shows 820 NAS allocated for carrier embarkation between 2018-2026 and 814 (and now 829) NAS specialising in providing aircraft for RFAs and frigates. 824 NAS is the training unit for all anti-submarine aircrew, ASaC 'Crowsnest' and commando Merlin pilots. 'Crowsnest' fitted Merlins, in which anti-submarine role equipment can be replaced by ASaC sensors and consoles, are being delivered by Leonardo helicopters. ASaC observer training will be carried out by the HQ Flight of 849 NAS and operational aircraft were allocated to TAGs in 2021. The Merlin Mk2, as part of the the Crowsnest programme, has replaced the Navy's Sea King Mk7 Airborne Surveillance and Control of 849 Naval Air Squadron (now retired) – and like their predecessors will be based at Royal Naval Air Station Culdrose, which also provides anti-submarine Merlin aircraft to protect the Fleet.

Crowsnest

Crowsnest is the name given to the Merlin Helicopters fitted with a large inflatable radome commonly known as 'baggers' in the Royal Navy. These helicopters provide airborne aerial surveillance and the control of other aircraft (known as ASAC). Inside the radome is the Lockheed Martin Searchwater Radar that, from its airborne position, can detect threats well in advance of shipborne sensors and increase the reaction time of the ships defences and complement. In the 1950s and until 1978 with the withdrawal of the last British conventional aircraft carrier ARK ROYAL the role was performed by Fairey Gannet AEW aircraft and then following the Falklands War of 1982 by Sea Kings of 849 Naval Air Squadron. With the withdrawal of the Sea Kings from service the role passed to the Merlin equipped Fleet Air Arm.

Crowsnest has experienced a troubled development programme. The contract with Lockheed Martin was placed in 2016, who subcontracted the work to Thales and Leonardo Helicopters. The high-risk programme quickly fell behind and scheduled milestones were routinely being missed. The IOC (initial operating capability) slipped 18 months to September 2021, four months after QUEEN ELIZABETH sailed on her historic first operational deployment to the Far East. Some elements of Crowsnest were available for the deployment but not the complete required package that linked the Searchwater Radar with the Cerberus mission system. The latest IOC issued by the MoD is for some time in 2023 with full operational capability to be declared some time later.

Such is the pace of technological innovation and development there is already talk of Crowsnest's possible future replacement. The Royal Air Force is at the early stages of  developing the ALVINA swarming drone for use with its fleet of Typhoon and F-35B jet fighters. These swarms will operate to act as decoys, distraction and electronic jamming roles in contested aerial environments. It is likely similar systems will be proposed for Project PROTEUS, a plan to develop a mid-sized RWAS capable of carrier operation and hunting submarines via sonobuoy and dipping sonar, in addition to providing a replacement for Crowsnest in the longer term. The RWAS will also contribute to the Maritime Intra-Theatre Lift (MITL).

By 2029 Project PROTEUS is projected to have matured sufficiently to release 'the expensive to operate' Merlin fleet from Crowsnest duties and allow them to concentrate on tracking and attacking enemy submarines. There have, however, been doubts raised about how such a system could be developed in the space of just 8 years given the developmental history of the Crowsnest system.

Leonardo Helicopters WILDCAT HMA2

Roles: Surface search and strike; anti-submarine strike; boarding party support
Engines: 2 x LHTEC CTS 800 each developing 1,362 shp
Length: 50' **Rotor diameter:** 42' **Height:** 12'
Max. Weight: 13,200lb **Max. Speed:** 157 knots **Crew:** 1 pilot & 1 observer
Avionics: Selex-Galileo Sea Spray 7400E multi-mode AESA radar; Wescam MX-15 electro-optical/IR camera; Electronic warfare system and defensive aids suite. Bowman communications system
Armament: 2 x Stingray torpedoes or Mark 11 depth charges; 1 x M3M 0.5" machine-gun in cabin door. From 2020 to carry Martlet (light) and Sea Venom (heavy) air-to-surface guided weapons.

Squadron Service: 815, 825 Naval Air Squadrons

Notes: 825 NAS is the training and tactical development unit and 815 NAS deploys flights of 1 or 2 aircraft to destroyers, frigates and some RFAs that do not embark Merlins. Wildcat is designed around a digital avionics management system that enhances mission effectiveness and reduces aircrew workload. Its 'paperless' maintenance system is shared with the Wildcat AH 1 operated by the Joint Helicopter Command. With the Lynx HMA 8 withdrawn from service in 2017, Wildcats now fully equip these two naval air squadrons which are both shore-based at RNAS Yeovilton. The HMA 2 has a significant strike capability since the Martlet and Sea Venom air-to-surface guided weapons achieved initial operational capability. Each Wildcat helicopter is capable of carrying 20 Martlett missiles. With the withdrawal from service of 700X NAS ScanEagle detachments in 2017, Wildcats and Merlins are the only air assets capable of deployment in destroyers, frigates and RFAs.In October 2021, HMS DEFENDER'S Wildcat helicopter from 815 Naval Air Squadron fired a Martlet missile – the first time the lightweight missile has been fired by the Royal Navy on frontline operations.

Grob TUTOR T1

Role: Elementary training
Engine: 1 x Textron Lycoming AE10-360-B1F developing 180 hp
Length: 24' 9" **Wingspan:** 32' 9" **Height:** 7'
Max. Weight: 2,178lb **Max. Speed:** 185 knots **Crew:** 2 pilots
Avionics: None
Armament: None

Squadron Service: 727 Naval Air Squadron, 703 Squadron MFTS

Notes: Tutors are used within Navy Command for the grading of potential aircrew and, in the short term, to clear a backlog in the MFTS. They provide elementary flying training for up to 12 student pilots per year. 703 Squadron is not a naval air squadron although it is numbered in what was until recently an exclusively naval sequence. It is part of the MFTS, providing elementary pilot training at RAF Barkston Heath for RN and RM pilots and Phase 1 and 2 training for RN observers. The aircraft is constructed mainly from carbon fibre reinforced plastic, which combines high strength with light weight. It has side-by-side seating with the primary flight instruments on the right-hand side of the cockpit.Thus, the student flies the aircraft from the right-hand seat with a right-hand stick and a left-hand throttle making transition to operational aircraft easier.

● CROWN COPYRIGHT/MOD

Lockheed Martin F-35B LIGHTNING II

Role: Strike, fighter and reconnaissance aircraft
Engine: 1 X Pratt & Whitney F135-PW-600 delivering 41,000lb thrust with reheat in conventional flight; 40,650lb hover thrust with Rolls-Royce lift fan engaged and tail nozzle rotated.
Length: 51' 4"   **Wingspan:** 35'   **Height:** 15'
Max. Weight: 60,000lb **Max. Speed:** Mach 1.6 **Crew:** 1 pilot
Avionics: AN/APG-81 AESA radar; AN/AAQ-40 electro-optical targeting system; AN/AAQ-37 distributed aperture system; AN/ASQ-239 'Barracuda' electronic warfare system; pilot's helmet-mounted display system; multi-function advanced data link.
Armament: Current Block 2B software allows the stealthy carriage of weapons in 2 internal bays with a single ASRAAM or AMRAAM air-to-air missile plus a single 1,000lb bomb equivalent such as Paveway IV LGB in each. Block 3F software in operational aircraft delivered from 2017 will enable the additional use of 7 non-stealthy external pylons, 3 under each wing and 1 under the centreline. A total of 12,000lb of weapons or fuel tanks to be carried; inner wing pylons have 'plumbing' for 426 US gallon drop tanks.

Squadron Service: 17, 207, 617 Squadrons.

Notes: The F-35B Lightning II Joint Strike Fighter is a multi-national Fifth Generation fighter aircraft that provides the Royal Navy with its fleet defence and strike capability operating from the Queen Elizabeth-class aircraft carriers. Britain is the sole Tier One Country alongside the Americans, and over 25,000 British jobs are dependent upon the programme. It also injects around £35 billion into the British economy. Originally, the MoD committed to purchasing a total of 138 F-35B Lightnings from Lockheed Martin over the lifetime of the programme which would have been delivered in batches. This number has, however, been whittled down until now the RN/RAF will receive just 48 examples of the type. This number is somewhat misleading as three of the British aircraft are test examples that are based in the United States and will never leave the USA.

JOINT FORCE LIGHTNING

The UK received six F-35Bs in 2022 and a further seven are due to be delivered in 2023. The schedule after these dates is uncertain following a temporary shutdown in production at Lockheed Martin after the discovery that a critical component in the aircraft's construction was being sourced from China.

The F-35Bs are jointly operated by the Fleet Air Arm and the Royal Air Force. Towards the end of 2023 we will see Royal Navy 809 Naval Air Squadron stood up for service. 809 Naval Air Squadron has an illustrious history having been involved in the invasions of North Africa, Italy and Southern France during World War 2 and later in November 1956 saw active service during Operation Musketeer during the Suez Crisis. After flying from the decks of the aircraft carriers HERMES and INVINCIBLE in the Falklands War the squadron was disbanded 17 December 1982.

CROWN COPYRIGHT/MOD   F-35B

What is the cowling right behind the cockpit used for?
The F-35B short takeoff and vertical landing (STOVL) capabilities are made possible through the Rolls-Royce patented shaft-driven LiftFan propulsion system installed behind the jet's cockpit, and an engine that can swivel 90 degrees when in short takeoff/vertical landing mode. When the jet is set to 'Lift' mode two doors open behind the cockpit, one being the cowling for the air intake for the 50-inch titanium LiftFan. The cowling opens only when hovering, short take-offs, or landing vertically. It directs air down into the LiftFan and closes during normal flight covering the lift fan. The smaller doors behind the big cowling gives additional clean air to the engine which is operating high during this time.

Leonardo Helicopters MERLIN HC3, HC3i, HC4

Role: Commando assault, load-lifting, troop movement
Engines: 3 x Rolls Royce/Turbomeca RTM 322 each developing 2,100 shp
Length: 74' 10" **Rotor diameter:** 61' **Height:** 21' 10"
Max. Weight: 32,120lb **Max. Speed:** 167 knots **Crew:** 1 or 2 pilots, 1 aircrewman
Avionics: Wescam MX-15 electro-optical/IR camera; defensive aids suite including directional IR countermeasures, AN/AAR-57 missile approach warning system, automatic chaff and flare dispensers
Armament: 1 x M3M 0.5" machine-gun in cabin door; 1 x 7.62mm machine-gun in cabin window

Squadron Service: 845, 846 Naval Air squadrons.

Notes: The first of 25 Merlin HC3s to be modified to HC4 standard was delivered by Leonardo Helicopters in 2017 and the last was due to be delivered in 2020, restoring an embarked capability to the Commando Helicopter Force, CHF. 7 aircraft have been modified to an interim HC3i standard to give some TAG capability until sufficient HC4s are available. The HC4 has a 'glass cockpit' similar to that of the HM2, power-folding main rotor head and tail pylon together with improved communications and defensive aids. Unlike the green HC3s, Merlin HC4s are painted grey. 845 NAS is eventually to have 10 aircraft deployable in up to 3 TAGs and 846 NAS is also to have 10 with an operational conversion/training flight, a maritime counter-terrorism flight and, after 2020, a TAG flight to back up 845. The remaining 5 airframes give deep maintenance flexibility and will act as attrition reserves.

The Merlin helicopter does not have the capability to lift and transport a jet engine for the F-35 which causes issues at the MoD. Due to funding constraints the MoD does not have a solution despite the Maritime Intra-theatre Lift Capability requiring the need to move people and equipment, especially parts for the F-35.

JOINT HELICOPTER COMMAND

Leonardo Helicopters WILDCAT AH1

Role: Battlefield reconnaissance; airborne command and control, force protection and troop transport.
Engines: 2 x LHTEC CTS 800-4N turboshafts each developing 1,362 shp
Length: 50' **Rotor diameter:** 42' **Height:** 12'
Max. Weight: 13,200lb **Max. Speed:** 157 knots **Crew:** 2 pilots & 1 gunner
Avionics: L-3 Wescam MX-15Di electro-optical/laser designator turret; digital mission planning system; Selex HIDAS 15 electronic warfare system
Armament: Door-mounted 0.5 inch M3M machine gun.

Squadron Service: 847 Naval Air Squadron, 1 Regiment Army Air Corps

Notes: 847 NAS is shore-based at RNAS Yeovilton and operates the Wildcat AH 1 as part of the Commando Helicopter Force, within the Joint Helicopter Command, to support 3 Commando Brigade with battlefield reconnaissance and airborne command and control of forces on the ground. 1 Regiment is also based at RNAS Yeovilton and operates, effectively, as a joint force with the RN Wildcat squadrons. It comprises a headquarters squadron plus 652, 659 and 661 Squadrons which operate their Wildcats as a specialised intelligence, surveillance and reconnaissance aircraft in support of troops on the ground. In the troop-lift role, Army Wildcats can lift up to 5 fully-equipped troops over short distances. Like 847 NAS they can be embarked to form part of a TAG when required and AAC pilots are trained to operate from the sea.

Leonardo Helicopters APACHE AH1

Role: Attack and armed reconnaissance helicopter
Engines: 2 x Rolls Royce/Turbomeca RTM 322 turboshafts each developing 2,100 shp
Length: 58' 3" **Rotor diameter:** 48' **Height:** 15' 3"
Max. Weight: 15,075lb **Max. Speed:** 150 knots **Crew:** 2 pilots
Avionics: Selex HIDAS defensive aids suite; Longbow radar; optical and infrared target indication sensors.
Armament: Up to 16 AGM-114 Hellfire air-to-surface guided weapons; up to 4 Sidewinder air-to-air missiles; M230 30mm cannon with 1,160 rounds; up to 76 CRV-7 unguided air-to-surface missiles.

Squadron Service: 3 and 4 Regiments Army Air Corps

Notes: 3 Regiment AAC comprises 653, 662 and 663 Squadrons. 4 Regiment comprises 656 and 664 Squadrons and both formations are based at the AAC base at RAF Wattisham and form part of the Joint Helicopter Command. Apaches of 656 Squadron flew successfully on operations over Libya with a TAG embarked in OCEAN during 2011 and at least one unit is maintained at high readiness for embarked operations as part of a TAG but in an emergency a larger number of Apaches could be embarked if required.

The Apache AH1 is to reach its out-of-service date in 2024 and be replaced by the Boeing AH-64D Apache Longbow attack helicopter. In 2021 the MoD decided on the weaponry for the Army Apache which can operate from the Navy's two carriers. The Lockheed Martin AGM-179 joint air-to-ground missile has been selected. Apache will also be equipped with Hellfire K-1 and Romeo missiles.

Boeing CHINOOK HC4, HC4A and HC5

Role: Battlefield transport helicopter
Engines: 2 x Avco Lycoming T55-L-712 turboshafts each developing 3,750 shp
Length: 98' 9" **Rotor diameter:** 60' **Height:** 18' 8"
Max. weight: 50,000lb **Max. speed:** 160 knots **Crew:** 2 pilots & 2 aircrewmen/gunners
Avionics: Infrared jammer; missile warning system; integrated digital 'glass cockpit'; moving map tablet and improved crewman's work station.
Armament: up to 2 M 134 mini guns mounted in doorways; one M 60 machine gun on rear loading ramp.

Squadron Service: 7, 18, 27, 28(AC) Squadrons Royal Air Force

Notes: All 4 squadrons are based at RAF Odiham from where the 3 operational units can provide TAG detachments when required. The Chinook's rotor blades cannot fold but QUEEN ELIZABETH's side lifts are large enough to strike down the aircraft, fully spread, into the hangar and they can be embarked in significant numbers to support both amphibious, military and humanitarian operations. Chinooks can carry 54 fully-equipped troops, 24 stretcher cases or loads up to 44,000lb carried both internally and externally over short distances. With extra fuel tanks they have a range of 1,000nm with a light load. Originally designed for the US Army, Chinooks are in widespread service throughout the world. The Boeing Chinook Helicopter entered service on the 22nd November 1980. Throughout its 40+ years of service the Chinook has made an immeasurable contribution to the Service, supporting communities across the UK and operating in every major conflict since the Falklands War.

SCHIEBEL S-100 CAMCAMPTOR

Role: Situational awareness and reconnaissancee
Wingspan: 3.4m **Weight:** 110kg **Top speed:** 222kph
Range: 180 miles **Armament:** None
Squadron Service: 700X Naval Air Squadron

Notes: On 10 February 2023 it was announced that the Royal Navy had selected Thales and Schiebel to provide a new rotary-wing Unmanned Aerial Vehicle (UAS) for use onboard Type 23 frigates under the terms of its Peregrine programme. Previously known as the Flexible Tactical Uncrewed Air System (FTUAS), Peregrine will see the Schiebel S-100 Camcopter equipped with a Thales I-Master radar to act as an additional eye in the sky to enhance the situational awareness of deployed Type 23 frigates. The system was selected as an urgent capability requirement.

AEROVIRONMENT RQ-20 PUMA

Role: Survey and reconnaissance **Length:** 4.6ft (1.4m) **Wingspan:** 9.2ft (2.8m)
Weight: 14lb (6.3kg) **Endurance:** 3+ hours and 15 miles range **Armament:** None
Squadron Service: 700X Naval Air Squadron

Notes: This hand launched drone is being operated by 700X Naval Air Squadron from its base at RNAS Culdrose whose role is to develop a strategy, resources and training within the Royal Navy to deploy these aircraft in the future. To this end they run two different courses, the first which is run 10 times annually instructs 150 personnel in the use of drones generally. The second course is dedicated to those personnel who will operate the RQ-20 PUMA. Puma AE (All Environment) is a fully waterproof, small, unmanned aircraft system (UAS) designed for land and maritime operations. Capable of landing in water or on land, the Puma AE empowers the operator with an operational flexibility never before available in the small UAS class. The enhanced precision navigation system with secondary GPS provides greater positional accuracy and reliability. AV's common ground control system allows the operator to control the aircraft manually or programme it for GPS based autonomous navigation.

EVOLVE DYNAMIC'S SKY MANTIS

Role: Survey and reconnaissance **Engines:** 4 x Electric Motors **Armament:** None
Squadron Service: 700X Naval Air Squadron

Notes: Described as a Rapid Response/Deployment Medium Size Multi Rotor Surveillance & Special Mission drone, the Evolve Dynamics' Sky Mantis can operate in a variety of weather conditions including heavy rain and windspeeds up to 75 kmh (46 mph or 40 knots). The drone carries a Dual HD 30X zoom low light EO and 640x512 30FPS thermal imaging camera as standard. The system, the manufacturers claim, can be operational within 1 minute and can fly for 1 hour with onboard battery power. The payload of the drone can be customisable for photography, mapping, survey and even gas sniffer roles. The Sky Mantis has been extensively tested onboard HMS PROTECTOR.

BAE Systems HAWK T2

Role: Advanced fast-jet training aircraft for RAF, RN and RM pilots
Engine: 1 x Rolls Royce Adour 951 FADEC/turbofan delivering 6,500lb of thrust
Length: 41' **Wingspan:** 32' 7" **Height:** 13' 1"
Max. Weight: 20,000lb **Max. Speed:** Mach 1 at altitude **Crew:** 1 or 2 pilots
Avionics: Two mission computers host simulations of sensor and weapons systems; a data link allows synthetic radar inputs for intercept training and synthetic electronic warfare threats. Inertial and GPS navigation systems.
Armament: 7 hardpoints capable of carrying a total of 6,800lb of weapons, including 1 x 30mm cannon pod on centreline, AIM-9 Sidewinder or ASRAAM missiles and bombs.

Squadron Service: 100 Squadron RAF

Notes: 4 (Reserve) Squadron forms part of Number 4 Flying Training School at RAF Valley within the Military Flying Training System and provides advanced fast-jet training for RAF, RN and RM pilots up to the standard required for conversion onto operational types. The Hawk T 2 has a 'glass cockpit' with 3 full-colour, multi-function displays, similar to those in the Typhoon and F-35B, which display navigation, weapons and system information intended to immerse student pilots into a complex, data-rich tactical flying environment from the outset rather than just learning to fly the aircraft.

In October 2021, 736 NAS was disbanded due to the retirement of the Hawk T1 and 100 Squadron RAF assumed maritime training support flying the Hawk T Mark II.

Short TUCANO T1

Role: Basic fast-jet training aircraft for RAF, RN and RM pilots
Engine: 1 x Garrett TPE 331-12B turboprop delivering 1,100 shp
Length: 32' 4" **Wingspan:** 37' **Height** 11' 2"
Max. Weight: 7,220lb **Max. Speed:** 300 knots **Crew:** 1 or 2 pilots
Avionics: Standard communications fit
Armament: None

Squadron Service 72(R) Squadron Royal Air Force

Notes: Operated by 72 (Reserve) Squadron as part of Number 1 Flying Training School at RAF Linton-on-Ouse, an element of the Military Flying Training System, the Tucano provides basic training for student RAF, RN and RM fast-jet pilots and RAF weapons system operators; it handles like a jet aircraft but is significantly cheaper to operate. Plans to replace the Tucano with the Beechcraft T-6C Texan II in 2019 have been delayed.

Beech AVENGER T1

Role: Observer training
Engines: 2 x Pratt & Whitney PT6A-60A, each developing 1,050 shp
Length: 46' 8" Wingspan: 57' 11" Height: 14' 4"
Max. Weight: 15,000lb Max. Speed; 313 knots
Crew: 1 or 2 pilots, 4 student observers plus instructors
Avionics: Surface search and ground mapping radar
Armament: None

Squadron Service: 750 Naval Air Squadron

Notes: Avengers are civil-owned but military registered and used by 750 NAS at RNAS Culdrose as part of the MFTS. They provide Phase 3 training for RN observers and lead-in training for RAF AWACS systems operators. Phases 1 and 2 of the Observer Course are carried out by 703 Squadron at RAF Barkston Heath.

CROWN COPYRIGHT/MOD

Airbus JUNO HT1

Role: Basic helicopter training
Engines: 2 x Turbomeca Arrius 2B, each developing 708 shp
Length: 39' 7" Rotor diameter: 33' 5" Height: 12' 4"
Max. Weight: 6,570lb Max. Speed: 140 knots
Crew: 2 pilots plus up to 6 passengers
Avionics: Defensive aids simulator; L-3 Wescam electro/optical camera
Armament: None

Squadron Service: 705 Squadron MFTS

Notes: The Juno HT1 began flying training at the Defence Helicopter School at RAF Shawbury in April 2018, replacing the Squirrel HT1. With twin engines and a night-vision goggle compatible glass cockpit, the helicopter gives student pilots a better lead-in to operational types such as the Merlin and Wildcat than its predecessors. All 29 Junos are fitted with a defensive aids simulator operated by the instructor and wired for an electro/optical camera installation although at any one time only 10 will be so fitted with the aim of teaching students to operate, rather than just fly modern aircraft types.

Eurocopter AS365N DAUPHIN 2

Role: Passenger movement and training support
Engines: 2 x Turbomeca Arriel 2C each developing 838 shp
Length: 39' 9" **Rotor diameter:** 39' 2" **Height:** 13' 4"
Max. Weight: 9,480lb **Max. Speed:** 155 knots **Crew:** 1 or 2 pilots plus up to 11 passengers
Avionics: None
Armament: None

Notes: Similar to the H-65 helicopters operated by the US Coast Guard, 2 of these civil-owned military-registered, COMR, helicopters are operated for the RN by Babcock Mission Critical Services Offshore Limited (known as Bond Offshore Helicopters until 25 April 2016) under contract. They are maintained at Newquay airport and used to support FOST in the sea areas off Plymouth. They are commonly tasked to transfer passengers between ships at sea but can also undertake a wide variety of other roles. On a day-to-day basis they fly from an operating facility within Devonport Naval base from which FOST staff can be flown from their headquarters directly to ships at sea.

Babcock operates a mixed fleet of helicopters on behalf of more than 10 major customers, specialising in providing offshore helicopter transportation services to North Sea and Irish Sea oil and gas platforms.

FLAG OFFICER SEA TRAINING COMMAND

Weapons of the Royal Navy

Sea Launched Missiles

Trident II D5

The American built Lockheed Martin Trident 2 (D5) submarine launched strategic missiles are Britain's only nuclear weapons and form the UK contribution to the NATO strategic deterrent. 16 missiles, each capable of carrying up to 6 UK manufactured thermonuclear warheads (but currently limited to 4 under current government policy), can be carried aboard each of the Vanguard-class SSBNs. Trident has a maximum range of 12,000 km and is powered by a three stage rocket motor. Launch weight is 60 tonnes, overall length and width are 13.4 metres and 2.1 metres respectively.

Tomahawk (BGM-109)

This is a land attack cruise missile with a range of 1600 km and can be launched from a variety of platforms including surface ships and submarines. Some 65 of the latter version were purchased from America to arm Trafalgar-class SSNs with the first being delivered to the Royal Navy for trials during 1998. Tomahawk is fired in a disposal container from the submarine's conventional torpedo tubes and is then accelerated to its subsonic cruising speed by a booster rocket motor before a lightweight F-107 turbojet takes over for the cruise. Its extremely accurate guidance system means that small targets can be hit with precision at maximum range, as was dramatically illustrated in the Gulf War and Afghanistan. Total weight of the submarine version, including its launch capsule is 1816 kg, it carries a 450 kg warhead, length is 6.4 metres and wingspan (fully extended) 2.54 m. Fitted in Astute & T-class submarines. It was announced in 2014 that the US Navy are to stop procuring the missile in 2015 which has implications for the production line, although an MoD spokesman expected this not to impact on UK requirements.

Harpoon

The Harpoon is a sophisticated surface-to-surface missile using a combination of inertial guidance and active radar homing to attack targets out to a range of 130 km, cruising at Mach 0.9 and carrying a 227 kg warhead. It is powered by a lightweight turbojet but is accelerated at launch by a booster rocket. Fitted to Type 23 frigates and four Type 45 destroyers. Harpoon was planned to be retired from Royal Navy service at the end of 2018, but this was extended to 2023. The future anti-ship missile system, a joint UK/French programme, will not be in service until 2030 at the very earliest.

Naval Strike Missile

For well over three decades the main long range striking weapon of the Royal Navy's surface fleet was the American Harpoon anti-ship missile. The current inventory of this weapon, however, is fast approaching its out-of-service date which had left a major hole in the Royal Navy's offensive strike capability. The Ministry of Defence (MoD) however has secured a deal with the Norwegian arms manufacturer Kongsberg Defence and Aerospace to acquire the Naval Strike Missile (NSM) which has been put into service with several other NATO navies including the US Navy. The NSM is a long range (greater than 100 nautical miles) anti-ship missile and carries a 500 pound class warhead with a programmable fuze. The missiles are capable of evading enemy defences and fly at sea-skimming level. The missiles are being rushed into service and will be fitted to 11 Type 23 frigates and all six Type 45 destroyers.

Sea Viper (Aster 15/30)

Two versions of the Aster missile equip the Type 45 Destroyer, the shorter range Aster 15 and the longer range Aster 30. The missiles form the weapon component of the Principal Anti Air Missile System (PAAMS). Housed in a 48 cell Sylver Vertical Launch system, the missile mix can be loaded to match the ships requirement. Aster 15 has a range of 30 km while Aster 30 can achieve 100 km. The prime external difference between the two is the size of the booster rocket attached to the bottom of the missile. PAAMS is known as Sea Viper in RN service.

In December 2022 the UK Government joined representatives of France and Italy and signed an agreement to develop the Aster 30 missile into a maritime ballistic defence variant. The UK's stock of missiles will be converted to the Aster 30 B1 Naval UK standard which will see further enhancements of the autopilot software and logistical updates. The work will be carried out at Defence Munitions, Gosport

Sea Wolf

Short range rapid reaction anti-missile and anti-aircraft weapon. The complete weapon system, including radars and fire control computers, is entirely automatic in operation. Type 23 frigates carry 32 Vertical Launch Sea Wolf (VLS) in a silo on the foredeck. Basic missile data: weight 82 kg, length 1.9 m, wingspan 56 cm, range c.5-6 km, warhead 13.4 kg. The VLS missile is basically similar but has jettisonable tandem boost rocket motors. The Sea Wolf system is gradually being replaced by Sea Ceptor.

Sea Ceptor

Incorporating the Common Anti-Air Modular Missile (CAMM) family, being developed to replace the Rapier and Sea Wolf SAM systems, plus the ASRAAM short range Air-to-Air Missile. It will arm the Royal Navy's Type 23 frigates and its Type 26 Global Combat Ships. In Spring 2012 the MoD awarded MBDA UK a five-year Demonstration Phase contract worth £483 million to develop the missile for the RN. In September 2013 a £250 million contract was announced to manufacture the missile in the UK, sustaining around 250 jobs at MBDA sites in Stevenage, Filton and Lostock. Installation of the Sea Ceptor on Type 23 frigates started in 2015 with ARGYLL and the last one was scheduled to be completed by 2021 but this has now been delayed. CAMM missiles will be fitted in the existing VL Sea Wolf silo (one canister per cell for a maximum of 32 missiles).

The first Sea Ceptor-enhanced Type 45 is expected to be delivered by the summer of 2026 with the entire flotilla completed by winter 2032. That is six ships updated over a six-year period.

Sea Venom

Formerly known as the Future Anti-Surface Guided Weapon (Heavy), Sea Venom is a high-subsonic 'drop-launch' missile in the 110 kg-class incorporating an imaging infrared seeker (with provisions for an additional semi-active laser guidance channel), a two-way datalink for operator-in-the-loop control, and a 30kg warhead. Designed by MBDA to replace the helicopter air-launched Exocet, the missile will have a range of up to 25 km and will be able to counter targets up to corvette size. The FASGW programme, comprising both Heavy and Light missiles, is a joint venture between the UK and France. The missile will equip the RNs Wildcat helicopter. In July 2014, AgustaWestland received a £90 million contract to integrate the respective variants for deployment from the Wildcat HMA2. Each aircraft will be able to carry four missiles and Initial Operating Capability was achieved in 2020.

Martlet

Formerly known as the Future Anti-Surface Guided Weapon (Light), this missile is designed to counter small boat and fast inshore attack craft threats. It is based on the laser beam-riding variant of the Thales Lightweight Multi-role Missile (LMM). With a range of up to 8 km it carries a 3 kg blast fragmentation/shaped charge warhead travelling at about Mach 1.5. Missiles will be carried in a five-round launcher (with each Wildcat able to carry up to four launchers). Alternatively a mix of two Sea Venom on the outer pylon and two five round Martlet on the inner weapons station can be carried. An active laser guidance unit integrated within the L-3 Wescam nose turret will support laser beam-riding guidance.

Guns

BAE 127mm (5") 62 calibre (Mk45) lightweight gun

Used by the US Navy in various calibres since 1953 this 5-inch gun mount will be installed on the Type 26 frigates. Originally designed and built by United Defense in the United States, until that company was bought by BAE Systems Land & Armaments in June 2005. The Royal Navy version consists of a longer-barrel L62 Mark 36 gun fitted to the same Mark 45 mount that provides firepower on the Type 23 frigates and Type 45 destroyers. The ammunition and firing sequences can be remotely controlled from the operations room without operator intervention in the gun bay. It has a built-in test and self-diagnosis system. The gun will first be installed onboard HMS GLASGOW.

114mm Vickers Mk8 Mod 1

The Royal Navy's standard medium calibre general purpose gun which arms the Type 23 frigates and Type 45 destroyers. The Mod 1 is an electrically operated version of the original gun and is recognised by its angular turret. First introduced in 2001 it is now fitted in all Type 23 and Type 45 vessels. Rate of fire: 25 rounds/min. Range: 22,000 m. Weight of Shell: 21 kg.

BOFORS 57mm Mk 3

Another new gun system that will be a feature of the future Royal Navy is the Bofors 57mm Mk3 gun system that will be the main gun armament of the Type 31 frigates. Development of this weapon started in the early 1960s in Sweden as the SjöAutomatKanon (SAK) L/70 based on the 57mm SAK L/60 built in the post-war period for several navies. This was later developed into the Mk 2 and Mk 3 by United Defence and by new owners BAE Systems. Throughout the 1980s Oto Melera 76mm mount became synonymous with naval gunnery worldwide but the Bofors system continued to be developed with a focus on accuracy, low radar cross section from its gun mount and smart 3P ammunition capability (Pre-fragmented, Programmable, Proximity-fused) rounds. The gunner can select one of six modes before firing that can shower a target with lethal airbursts of tungsten pellets, high explosive or armour piercing rounds. But at £3,800 per round Smart Ammunition is not cheap. The Bofors 57mm Mk3 has been selected by the US Coast Guard to arm its new Legend-class National Security Cutters. The system is already used by Brunei, Canada, Finland, Germany, Indonesia, Malaysia, Mexico, Norway and Sweden.

BOFORS 40mm Mk 4

The Type 31 frigates will also introduce the first 40mm gun to the Royal Navy since the Bofors 40mm L/60 Mark IX that was last used in the late 1980s. In the intervening years the Royal Navy has standardised the 30mm small calibre gun. The 40mm weapon, however, offers increased lethality against aircraft and ships and longer range. Work on the Mk 4 started in 2009 and has led to a fully digitised modularised system that is ideal for shipbuilding on a budget such as the Type 31 frigates programme. Ten mounts for the five Type 31 frigates were ordered in October 2020 with the first expected to arrive at the Rosyth shipyard later in 2023.

DS30B 30mm

Single mounting carrying an Oerlikon 30mm gun. Fitted to Type 23 frigates and various patrol vessels and MCMVs. In August 2005 it was announced that the DS30B fitted in Type 23 frigates was to be upgraded to DS30M Mk 2 to include new direct-drive digital servos and the replacement of the earlier Oerlikon KCB cannon with the ATK Mk 44 Bushmaster II 30 mm gun. Consideration is already being given to purchasing additional DS30M Mk 2 systems for minor war vessels and auxiliaries.

Phalanx

A US-built CIWS designed around the Vulcan 20 mm rotary cannon. Rate of fire is 3000 rounds/min and effective range is c.1500 m. Fitted in Type 45 and some Wave, Bay and Fort Classes. Block 1B began entering service from 2009. Incorporates side mounted forward looking infra-red enabling CIWS to engage low aircraft and surface craft. In October 2012 it was announced that a further five Phalanx Block 1B mountings were to be procured to protect RFA ships.

GAM BO 20mm

A simple hand operated mounting carrying a single Oerlikon KAA 200 automatic cannon firing 1000 rounds/min. Maximum range is 2000 m. Carried by most of the fleet's major warships except the Type 23 frigates.

20mm Mk.7A

The design of this simple but reliable weapon dates back to World War II but it still provides a useful increase in firepower, particularly for auxiliary vessels and RFAs. Rate of fire 500-800 rounds/min.

Close Range Weapons

In addition to the major weapons systems, all RN ships carry a variety of smaller calibre weapons to provide protection against emerging terrorist threats in port and on the high seas such as small fast suicide craft. In addition it is sometimes preferable, during policing or stop and search operations to have a smaller calibre weapon available. Depending upon the operational environment ships may be seen armed with varying numbers of pedestal mounted

General Purpose Machine Guns (GPMG). Another addition to the close in weapons is the Mk 44 Mini Gun, a total of 150 of which have been procured from the United States as a fleetwide fit. Fitted to a naval post mount, the Minigun is able to fire up to 3,000 rounds per minute, and is fully self-contained (operating off battery power).

Dragonfire

Dragonfire is the Royal Navy's £130 million directed energy weapon system program that will be included in the weapons fit for the Type 26 frigates when they enter service. The system will also be fitted to RAF jets and to a variety of British Army combat vehicles. The first batch of the systems is currently undergoing extensive testing with lower energy outputs than production models against a variety of aerial targets.

Torpedoes

Sting Ray

A lightweight anti-submarine torpedo which can be launched from ships, helicopters or aircraft. In effect it is an undersea guided missile with a range of 11 km at 45 knots or 7.5 km at 60 knots. Length 2.1 m, diameter 330 mm. Type 23s have the Magazine Torpedo Launch System (MTLS) with internal launch tubes. Sting Ray Mod 1 is intended to prosecute the same threats as the original Sting Ray but with an enhanced capability against small conventionally powered submarines and an improved shallow-water performance.

Spearfish

Spearfish is a submarine-launched heavyweight torpedo which has replaced Tigerfish. Claimed by the manufacturers to be the world's fastest torpedo, capable of over 70 kts, its sophisticated guidance system includes an onboard acoustic processing suite and tactical computer backed up by a command and control wire link to the parent submarine. Over 20ft in length and weighing nearly two tonnes, Spearfish is fired from the standard 21-inch submarine torpedo tube and utilises an advanced bi-propellant gas turbine engine for higher performance. The Navy is investing £270m upgrading the Spearfish heavyweight torpedo by fitting a new warhead, a safer fuel system, an enhanced electronic brain and a fibre-optic guidance link with the parent submarine in order to improve accuracy and lethality. The warhead is at least six times more powerful than that carried by the Stringray lightweight torpedo. Enhanced Spearfish will be introduced to SSNs over the next three years and will be in service until the 2050s. Sea trials have recently been carried out with the frigate SUTHERLAND.

At the end of the line

HMS Severn (left) and HMS Belfast

HMS Echo

HMS ECHO

Survey ship HMS ECHO's 20-year Royal Navy career formally ended on 30 June 2022 at a decommissioning ceremony at Portsmouth Naval Base. The ship was the first of two Echo-class survey ships designed for hydrographic and oceanographic operations across the world.

HMS SABRE and SCIMITAR

The Royal Navy decommissioned patrol boats HMS SABRE and HMS SCIMITAR in a ceremony at Portsmouth Naval Base on 30 March 2022. The pair have spent nearly 30 years in service, serving in Northern Ireland in their early career and as guard ships with the Gibraltar Squadron from 2003 to late 2020. They were sold in September 2022 for civilian use.

HMS BLYTHE AND HMS RAMSEY

BLYTHE and RAMSEY were decommissioned in a joint ceremony at Rosyth on 4 August 2021. Following a refit by Babcock they will be transferred to the Ukrainian Navy. The Russian invasion of Ukraine has, however, meant that the date for the transfer of these warships has been put back until probably after the war. Both vessels have served extensively during their careers spanning 21 years and 175,000 miles for RAMSEY, and 185,000 miles over 20 years for BLYTH, supporting operations in the Middle East, around the UK or on NATO duties in northern European and Mediterranean waters. The ships are being replaced by the expanding Project WILTON to introduce autonomous/uncrewed boats and systems into minehunting – an initiative being pioneered at Faslane where three boats are already in service.

HMS SHOREHAM

Since last year's British Warships and Auxiliaries, the slow run down in the fleet of minesweepers and minehunters has begun with the decommissioning from service of the Sandown-class minehunter HMS SHOREHAM. She spent almost half of her Royal Navy career conducting operations in the Gulf region.

HMS Trenchant

HMS TALENT and HMS TRENCHANT

On 20 May 2022 in a rare double decommissioning of two Trafalgar-class nuclear powered submarines - HMS TALENT and sister submarine HMS TRENCHANT - were decommissioned at Devonport together in front of The Princess Royal, HMS TALENT's Royal patron. Both submarines served in the Royal Navy for 32-years.

GRIFFON 2400TD LCAC

Withdrawn from Royal Marine operations is Griffon LCAC, officially known as the Landing Craft Air Cushion (Light). The so-called 'floating fortress' can carry 16 marines and race across water, ice and mud. Operated by 539 Raiding Squadron, the 2400TD offers greater payload, performance and obstacle clearance than the earlier 2000TD craft. Centre sections of the cabin roof can be removed in order to embark two 1 tonnes NATO pallets. Similiar to the 2000TD, the 2400TD's design allows the user to reduce the width of the craft with foldable side decks allowing it to be transported on a standard low loader truck or in the hold of a C-130 Hercules aircraft. They can also operate directly from the well-deck of RN amphibious ships. They are equipped with a 7.62mm GPMG, HF and VHF radios, radar, GPS, ballistic protection and a variety of specialised equipment. They also produce next to no wake at high speed, which makes them more stealthy than traditional landing craft and with their powerful engines, much faster.

RFA DILLIGENCE

The Royal Navy's former forward repair vessel has, since 2016, been in reserve. Originally commissioned as a commercial oil rig support ship she was taken up from trade following the Falklands War, which identified the need for a forward repair ship to repair battle damaged warships in-situ and away from dockyard facilities. In 2020 a Royal Navy spokesperson said that DILLIGENCE was "an aged singleton ship with increasing obsolescence issues", and that it was no longer cost-effective to maintain her in service." The 2021 British Defence White Paper made no mention of the ship or her capabilities and after a spell at Birkenhead in reserve in March 2017 she was placed within Portsmouth Dockyard where she remains awaiting disposal, probably by scrapping.

HMS Montrose

HMS MONTROSE and HMS MONMOUTH

The UK's oldest in-service Type 23 frigates - HMS MONTROSE and HMS MONMOUTH - were declared surplus to requirement under the terms of the UK Integrated Review and Defence Command Paper. The UK Government planned for the two frigates to be gifted to the Greek Navy as part of efforts to sweeten a deal to build four new Type 31s for Greece, as well as Babcock International upgrading the Hellenic Navy's existing German-designed 30-year-old Hydra-class frigates. Unfortunately, the French government entered into a defence pact with Greece and agreed to sell frigates to the Greek Navy. HMS MONMOUTH is now laid up in Portsmouth Harbour awaiting either sale or scrap. Sistership HMS MONTROSE will join her as she is scheduled to be decommissioned in April 2023.

HMS QUORN

The Hunt-class mine-countermeasures vessel has been purchased for refitting for the Lithuanian Navy. The £55 million contract is being undertaken by Harland and Wolff shipyard at their Appledore, North Devon shipyard. She will on completion of the refit join two sister ships in service with the Lithuanian Navy, ex-DULVERTON and ex-COTTESMORE.

HMS ATHERSTONE

This Hunt-class mine-countermeasures vessel was decommissioned on 14 December 2017 and has languished in Portsmouth Harbour since then gradually being stripped of parts and equipment for the surviving members of the RN Hunt Class force to keep them operational. On 3 June 2020, the stripped down ATHERSTONE was advertised for sale. Harland and Wolff shipyard bought the vessel with the intention to rebuild it as a non-military vessel or alternatively as a source of spare parts in the refit of sister ship QUORN.

HMS WALNEY

The Sandown-class minehunter HMS WALNEY was decommissioned in 2010. She has been stripped of almost all useable equipment and propulsion systems while laid-up in Portsmouth Naval Base. Initially put up for sale for offers in excess of £30,000, DESA has now issued a notice of the potential sale of the former WALNEY for recycling only.

ENS Luxor (ex-RFA Fort Austin)

RFA FORT AUSTIN and RFA FORT ROSALIE
The former two 1978/79 sisters RFA FORT AUSTIN and RFA FORT ROSALIE had been laid-up in Birkenhead and looked to be destined for the scrap yard before the Egyptian Navy stepped in and acquired both vessels for further service from the MoD's Defence Equipment Sales Agency (DESA). The regeneration contract for the two vessels was placed in the hands of Cammell Laird because of the Birkenhead-based shipyard's deep and intimate knowledge of the two former Fort-class vessels, having been responsible for their drydocking and maintenance for many years under MoD Cluster Support and Future In-service Support (FISS) contracts.

The scope of work carried out on the two former RFAs' included significant overhaul of machinery and systems, drydocking and refit work, comprising the overhaul of each vessel's Crossley-Pielstick main engines, diesel generators, sea valves, propellors, anodes and thrusters. At the same time, the vessels were repainted. FORT ROSALIE has been renamed ENS ABU SIMBEL and FORT AUSTIN has been renamed ENS LUXOR.

ENS LUXOR was towed to Alexandria in the second half of last year. ENS ABU SIMBEL still remains alongside in Birkenhead, before being towed to Egypt in early 2023.

HMS BRISTOL
It is widely expected that BRISTOL, the sole Type 82 guided missile destroyer built, will be sold for scrap in 2023. Since the Royal Navy announced in February 2020 that the ship would no longer be used for training purposes her condition has deteriorated rapidly at her berth alongside Whale Island in Portsmouth Harbour. She commissioned into the Royal Navy in 1973 and served with distinction for 57 years including serving in the Falklands War. She is the last major British warship still afloat that fought in the South Atlantic and despite a campaign to preserve her as a museum, it seems extremely unlikely that she can be saved.

> *A National Audit Office report into the MoD's equipment plan 2019-2029 mentioned the defuelling and dismantling of redundant nuclear submarines. The MoD has deferred dismantling submarines on affordability grounds and has not disposed of any of the 20+ redundant submarines it has decommissioned since 1980. The MoD has not defuelled a nuclear submarine since 2004. With the decommissioning of TRENCHANT and TALENT it now stores eleven fuelled submarines...* **"**

At the end of the line ...

Readers may well find other warships afloat which are not mentioned in this book. The majority have fulfilled a long and useful life and are now relegated to non-seagoing duties. The following list gives details of their current duties:

Pennant No	Ship	Remarks
M29	BRECON	Hunt-class Minehunter - Attached to the New Entry Training Establishment, HMS Raleigh, Torpoint, as a static Seamanship Training Ship.
M103	CROMER	Single Role Minehunter - Attached to BRNC, Dartmouth as a Static Training Ship.
L3505	SIR TRISTRAM	Refitted as a Static Range Vessel at Portland.
S50	COURAGEOUS	Nuclear-powered Submarine - On display at Devonport Naval Base. Can be visited during Base Tours.
C35	BELFAST (1938)	World War II Cruiser Museum ship - Port of London Open to the public daily.
D73	CAVALIER	World War II Destroyer & Oberon-class Submarine
S17	OCELOT	Museum Ships at Chatham. Open to the public.
S67	ALLIANCE	Submarine - Museum Ship at Gosport Open to the public daily.
LCT7074	LANDFALL	A D-Day veteran. Refloated in October 2014 six years after she sank at Birkenhead. After years of extensive restoration by NMRN at Portsmouth she has been moved to Southsea and is on display outside the D-Day Museum.
	BRITANNIA	Ex Royal Yacht at Leith. Open to the public.
	CAROLINE	Light Cruiser and veteran of the Battle of Jutland preserved at Belfast.
	M33	Coastal Monitor and veteran of the Gallipoli Campaign on display at Portsmouth as part of the National Museum of the Royal Navy.